Date Du

The Cellular
Role of
Macromolecules

1~99

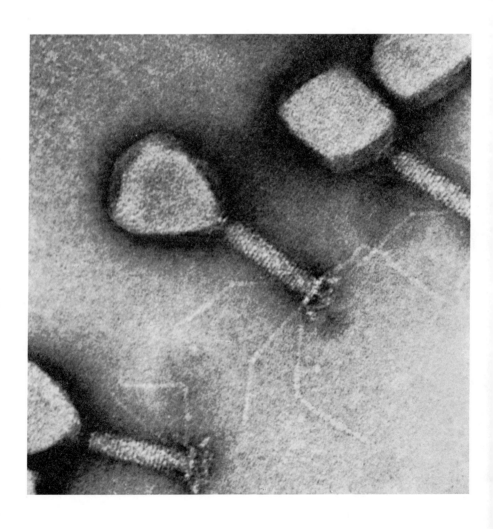

SCOTT, FORESMAN SERIES IN UNDERGRADUATE BIOLOGY

Samuel Matthews, *Williams College*, GENERAL EDITOR

The Cellular
Role of
Macromolecules

P. H. Jellinck

Queen's University, Kingston, Ontario

SCOTT, FORESMAN AND COMPANY

Library of Congress Catalog Card Number 67-15478
Copyright © 1967 by Scott, Foresman and Company, Glenview, Illinois 60025
All rights reserved. Printed in the United States of America.
Regional offices of Scott, Foresman and Company are located in Atlanta,
Dallas, Glenview, Palo Alto, and Oakland, N.J.

FOREWORD

In recent years interest in Biology has focused with increasing sharpness on two contrasting areas—the molecular basis of activities of cells and organisms and behavior and population studies. New concepts along with new and more precise methods of laboratory research have resulted in an explosive growth of information. This rapid increase of knowledge, which is doubling every two years, is the concern of all biologists. How may the changing emphasis in biology and the accompanying mass of new information be presented to the beginning student? How can he be adequately informed about areas necessary for further exploration, such as taxonomy, structure, and function, and at the same time be made aware of the new, conceptual dimensions of these areas? Such questions have caused considerable discussion, and suggestions for modification of the introductory course have ranged from abolishing it completely to making it entirely a problems course, with all the logistic and administrative difficulties such an approach would encounter.

One point seems clear. Early in his scientific studies the student must appreciate that science is a continually changing body of knowledge, not a fixed mass of information, and he must gain some concept of how growth in scientific understanding occurs. No clear method exists for achieving these objectives. Actual laboratory experience with someone actively engaged in research would be the most effective means, but opportunities of this kind can be provided for only a few students. Another approach, and one more readily available, would be to have each student read about such experiments, preferably in the words of the investigators themselves. In this way the student might look over the shoulders of those who are performing the experiments and gain some insight into how growth in understanding of the science is brought about.

There are two principal difficulties with the second suggested approach. First, adequate access to scientific journals would be difficult to provide. The cost of subscribing to and storing anything close to complete coverage of biological journals is prohibitive for most colleges, and the single copies of those journals available are woefully inadequate reading sources for large classes. Second, the language of scientific papers might confuse the beginning student. Careful selection and considerable annotation of material would clearly be necessary, and this alone would probably be inadequate. In order to appreciate the significance of newer studies in a particular area, the student would need a firm understanding of that area. Any treatment that would provide the background for such understanding for all the major segments into which biology has traditionally been divided (embryology, physiology, genetics, etc.) and which also would include a discussion of the newer concepts in these fields would need to be of formidable size. But could this be done for a few topics which are of fundamental significance to understanding present-day biology? And could these topics be presented in a form readily available to the student?

To test the possibility of this approach, a brief outline of the idea was sent to a number of biologists to invite their opinions. As a result of the interest shown, several agreed to undertake discussions of topics within their own areas of interest. This group met and discussed the objectives and nature of the series of volumes that would be prepared. The present series is the result of these efforts.

The topics chosen for discussion were selected in the belief that they exemplify the changing emphasis of modern biology. For each of these topics an attempt is made to establish fundamental principles and to indicate how the area is advancing by experimental work. There is a certain logic in the order of the volumes, proceeding as they do from ultrastructure, macromolecules, and the principles of biochemistry to physiological regulation and the biology of populations and evolution. Each volume, however, is complete in itself and may be used alone or in combination with some or all of the others, as the nature of the particular course and the objectives of a particular instructor dictate. In any case to provide either the terminal student with a sound grasp of the field or the biology major with an adequate background for further exploration, the topical approach utilized in this series would need to be supplemented by lectures on those areas of biology not covered in the volumes.

The Scott, Foresman Series in Undergraduate Biology is designed for use as basic texts for introductory biology courses, as useful supplementary material for lectures and laboratory work in other biology courses, and as review or supplementary sources for specialized, intermediate courses. It is hoped that these volumes may afford the student some idea of the recent and significant change in focus of biology and some concept of the excitement and challenge of this rapidly moving science.

Samuel A. Matthews, *Williams College*

PREFACE

Developments during the past decade have resulted in the realization that an inextricable relationship exists between cellular structure and function, and that the molecular machinery of the cell can be studied adequately only by fusing the more classical disciplines of biochemistry, biophysics, cytology, and cellular physiology.

One objective of this book is to convey the scope and dynamic nature of biochemistry to the reader and to introduce molecular biology at a relatively elementary level. The text deals essentially with the fundamental aspects of modern biochemistry as they apply to living organisms. No attempt has been made to cover all facets of this ever expanding field or to document all the exciting developments of recent years, but instead, certain topics of current interest have been highlighted and covered at some depth. Considerable effort has been made to blend cellular ultrastructure and physiology with organic chemistry, so that students in biology may be able to tread on familiar grounds while assimilating the more complex aspects of metabolism. In addition, an attempt has been made to keep in perspective the "classical" aspects of biochemistry without detracting from the very exciting recent developments in molecular biology.

With this approach, *The Cellular Role of Macromolecules* should provide an adequate background for students of biology wishing to probe deeper into the mechanisms of living processes and to learn about the limits of the subject and the many problems still outstanding.

The term "macromolecule" in the title has been chosen deliberately to stress that all biochemical processes even when involving simple molecules are carried out by complex molecular systems generally associated with ultrastructural components of the cell.

The names of many outstanding research workers have been mentioned in connection with their discoveries, and their individual contributions and philosophy have been shown by liberal quotations from their publications.

Finally, great effort has been made to achieve simplicity of presentation without detracting from accuracy or avoiding the controversies which, almost by definition, are present in "living" systems.

P. H. Jellinck, *Queen's University*

CONTENTS

CHAPTER 1 The Cell:
An Organized
System of
Macromolecules

Not so many years ago, the cell was visualized as a structureless mass of a mysterious gelatinous substance, *protoplasm*, surrounded by a membrane and endowed with the properties of life. In addition, it was known to contain a *nucleus* in which *chromosomes* could be seen during cell division. Any enzymes present were believed to be distributed in a random haphazard fashion. The cell, in fact, was regarded by most biochemists of those days merely as a "bag of enzymes."

Man's concepts of the cell have changed, however, with the advent of the electron microscope and the elegant ultrathin sectioning techniques developed by K. R. Porter and George E. Palade at the Rockefeller Institute and by F. S. Sjöstrand in Stockholm. The biochemist has become a biochemical cytologist, interested as much in the structure of the cell as in its biochemical activities. It is now recognized that certain enzymes are associated with certain membrane-bound structures (organelles) inside the cell, and that an elaborate organization exists even at this level. It appears that the cell contains a series of "microkitchens" which enable substrate molecules to coexist with their specific enzymes without interaction, until diffusion or active transport (see Vol. V of this series) into the appropriate subcellular compartments has occurred.

Electron microscopy has also raised many questions which could not even be phrased without this new look into the near-molecular level within cells. In addition, autoradiography using radioactive tracers (Chap. 2) has contributed much towards unraveling subcellular biochemical events.

Compared to atoms and molecules, the cell is a unit of great size and complexity. It has been calculated that the average mammalian cell can accommodate at least 100,000 million protein molecules and is, therefore, large enough to carry out a wide variety of reactions at the molecular level. A characteristic feature of cells is that they contain highly complex macromolecules which they are able to synthesize from simpler substances. The cell is also characterized by ceaseless chemical activity (metabolism) associated with maintaining both the integrity of its internal structure and the constancy of its internal environment. However, it must be emphasized that although most of the vital activities of living organisms, such as growth, reproduction, and the response to various stimuli, can now be analyzed in terms of molecular reactions, these processes are still far from being fully understood. If one wonders at the exquisite organization of molecules within the cellular microcosm and at their precisely geared interactions, one can only be filled with awe at the complexities of the more elaborate systems of multicellular plants and animals.

■ STRUCTURE AND FUNCTION OF THE CELL

The concept that the cell is the unit structure of plant and animal life is accepted universally now, although little more than a century has elapsed since Schleiden and Schwann first proposed the cell theory, and Virchow showed that only cells can give rise to new cells: "Omnis cellula e cellula." It is possible to break up cells and isolate component parts which carry out for a while many "normal" biochemical activities, but these reactions do not constitute life any more than subatomic particles represent the behavior of an intact atom. The cell is, therefore, the smallest portion of an organism that can sustain life independently and exhibit the range of properties associated with living matter. *Viruses*, which are infective "agents" capable of self-reproduction only within the living cell and which form an interesting link between cells and macromolecules, are considered later in this chapter.

Before discussing cells in general, it should be pointed out that no typical cells exist. All cells have their own individual characteristics which usually make it possible to determine from which organ or tissue a particular cell is derived. The size of the cell bears no relation to the size of its organ of origin, and large cells may be found in very small organisms. Thus the egg cells of birds are many times larger than the ova of the whale, and the single-celled alga, *Acetabularia*, may reach 9 to 10 cm in height. Different cells may also assume a great variety of shapes depending usually on their function, as exemplified by the elongated threadlike nerve cells, flattened epithelial cells, or the stinging hair cells of nettles.

In spite of all these diversities, however, cells of all types have certain constant features—they all are provided with cytoplasm, containing various organelles, a central nucleus, and a cell membrane. (*Fig. 1–1*) As an extreme oversimplification, the cytoplasm may be considered the factory of the cell in which substrate molecules are either broken down by appropriate enzymes to liberate energy or else built up into more complex substances needed by the cell for maintenance or multiplication. The main function of the nucleus is to control the biochemical activities of the cytoplasm and to transmit the cell's hereditary traits from one generation to the next (see also Vol. IV). Although the structure of the nucleus and cytoplasm generally are dealt with separately, it has been shown that in the intact cell structural continuity as well as functional relationship exists between the two. Before the detailed discussion of the architecture and biochemical role of the "cytoskeleton," the cell membrane and the means by which molecules penetrate it to get inside the cell will be considered.

■ **THE CELL MEMBRANE**

Although some sort of coating seems essential to maintain the integrity and shape of the cell in its liquid environment and to control constant exchange of material between inside and outside, very little was known about the structure of this coating until recently. This was because the cell membrane is far too thin to be visible even under the most powerful light microscope. However, even before visualiza-

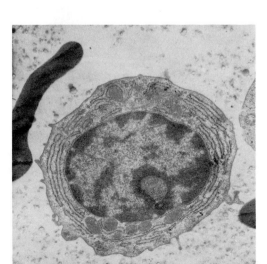

Fig. 1-1. Electron micrograph of a cell. (Courtesy Dr. W. H. Chase, University of British Columbia)

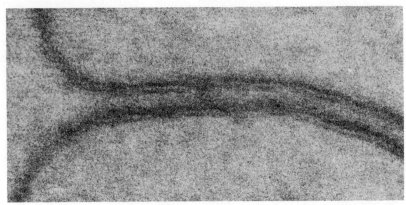

Fig. 1-2. Electron micrograph of a cell. Membranes of two cells in a mouse nerve fiber are enlarged 400,000 diameters in this electron micrograph by J. David Robertson of the Harvard Medical School. Each membrane is approximately 75 angstrom units thick and consists of two dense lines each 20 angstrom units wide separated by a light area 35 angstroms across. The gap between the cells is nearly 150 angstroms. The two dense lines of each membrane correspond to Danielli's protein component; the light area between them may be the lipid region. (From H. Holter, "How Things Get into Cells." Copyright © 1961 by Scientific American, Inc. All rights reserved.)

tion, the cell membrane was recognized to be elastic, pliable, and capable of growing as the cell enlarges. In addition, it was known to display some capacity for self-repair, sealing spontaneously any opening in it made by puncturing with a needle.

With the advent of the electron microscope, present-day models of which can easily resolve a macromolecular layer of protein, J. D. Robertson at Harvard was able to show the cell membrane and to assign to it a thickness of approximately 75 angstrom units* (Å). He called it the "unit membrane" to denote its cellular universality and gave support to the earlier model proposed by James F. Danielli of King's College, London. According to Danielli's model, the membrane consists of a double layer of lipid molecules covered by two protein layers. Electron micrographs (*Fig. 1–2*) show two electron-dense lines about 20 Å thick, which are believed to represent the two layers of protein, separated by a lighter area 35 Å across, corresponding to the lipid (mainly phospholipid) layers. It is believed that the phospholipid molecules are oriented parallel to each other and at right angles to the plane of the membrane, with their uncharged lipophilic portion pointing toward each other and their polar-charged hydrophilic groups associated with ionized groups of the protein (*Fig. 1–3*).

* One mm = 10^3 μ = 10^7 Å units.

The resulting structure has both hydrophilic and hydrophobic properties and gives the membrane a certain degree of elasticity and mechanical strength. What is more important, however, is that it endows the membrane with the property of *selective permeability*, enabling it, except under certain conditions, to keep out many molecules and ions. In addition, the membrane acts as a vectorial barrier in which the direction of flow of compounds is as important as their chemical nature. Because of this the suggestion has been made that there may be differences in the chemical nature of the inside and outside surfaces of the membrane, and that many cells may, in addition, possess a carbohydrate-rich overcoat of mucoprotein. In any case certain substances are known to penetrate the cell against a concentration gradient, but this process requires work; and, in fact, much of the energy of the cell is utilized in transporting material in and out of the cell across the membrane.

Such "active transport" (see also Vol. V), however, is not always required; and some materials, in particular small uncharged molecules, may pass through the cell membrane by simple *diffusion* from a more concentrated solution to a less concentrated one. Many compounds that dissolve easily in fats also pass readily through the cell membrane. Material also may be taken in by *pinocytosis* or "cell-drinking," a process in which the membrane invaginates to draw material into the cell and then pinches off to form tiny vacuoles around it.

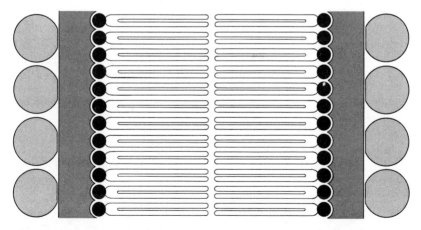

Fig. 1-3. Structure of unit membrane. "Butter Sandwich" version of membrane structure is schematically represented. Two layers of lipids, their fatty tails pointing in and their water-soluble heads pointing out, comprise the middle section. They lie between two thin sheets of protein *(medium gray bands)*. These sheets of protein are thought to be coated with globular proteins *(light gray circles)*. (From L. E. Hokin and M. R. Hokin, "The Chemistry of Cell Membranes." Copyright © 1965 by Scientific American, Inc. All rights reserved.)

Finally the membrane also may vary in structure laterally, since it behaves like a sieve to some types of molecules. However, there is no electron microscopic evidence so far for the existence of such openings.*

The same kind of membrane is present not only at the cell surfaces of all types of living organisms but also inside the cells, surrounding the nucleus and various organelles. These internal membranes also form the lining of the system of cytoplasmic canals known as the *endoplasmic reticulum*, and they are often folded in complicated ways with a tendency to associate in pairs. One of the most significant developments of recent years has been the recognition that these cellular membranes themselves may contain the macromolecular assemblies of enzymes.

More recently, however, E. A. Korn has questioned the universality of the unit membrane. He points out that membranes differ widely in chemical composition, metabolism, function, and enzymatic composition and suggests that until more is known about the chemistry of electron microscopy, evidence obtained from electron micrographs alone cannot be interpreted with confidence.

Concerning the evolution of the membrane, one is led to ask as did Robertson:

> Where did the first membrane come from? In speculation about the origin of life the emphasis has been on protein and nucleic acid. There has so far been little interest in the origin of lipids. Actually the production of lipid molecules may have been crucial to the origin of life. This is so because lipids in a watery medium tend to aggregate into thin continuous sheets. The primitive membrane would have served as a container for the various large molecules and as a surface on which they could be anchored and arranged in the integrated patterns that are as essential to life as the existence of the large molecules themselves. It seems highly probable that only after membranes appeared could the first living things be organized from the soup brewing in the ancient seas.[1]

Much remains to be discovered about the cell membrane, and one of the major problems is its formation in living organisms. This was recognized by D. E. Green and O. Hechter:

> The formation of a biological membrane may be presumed to be a stepwise process leading from proteins to polyprotein complexes, from complexes to functional subunits and finally to the membrane continuum. . . . How is this precision assembly problem achieved in

---

* These should not be confused with the pores formed by folding of the membrane surrounding the nucleus (*Fig. 1–7*).

accord with a predetermined blueprint? In a membrane system a spontaneous self-assembly process would imply that the proteins to be assembled, once liberated from the site of polysome synthesis, spontaneously interact in the aqueous environment of the cytoplasm to produce progressively more complex macromolecular structures. The alternative to a self-assembly process is one in which the "built in" specifications of the components to be assembled are insufficient to provide for precise assembly. If external devices for assembly are operative, we should like to know their nature and the mechanism whereby they are controlled by gene action.[2]

■ THE ENDOPLASMIC RETICULUM

In recent years Porter and Palade have shown by electron microscopy that some of the surface invaginations of the cell membrane continue into the depth of the cell and there form a system of canals and vesicles – the endoplasmic reticulum. This system of vesicles appears to be present in all plant and animal cells (except mammalian erythrocytes), including lower organisms such as the protozoa. In bacteria a variety of intracytoplasmic membrane structures have been reported, but these may not be related to the endoplasmic reticulum of higher forms.

The endoplasmic reticulum varies greatly in shape both from one cell type to another and also in different physiological and developmental stages of the same cell type. Two general kinds of endoplasmic reticulum have been described – the rough-surfaced type, also known as *ergastoplasm*, which has associated with it on its cytoplasmic side numerous electron-dense granules called *ribosomes*; and the smooth type, lacking ribosomes. These particles (diameter 150 Å) are rich in RNA (40 per cent by weight) and are involved in the synthesis of cellular protein (Chap. 4). When cells are broken up by homogenization and the cellular components separated by centrifugation, the so-called *microsomal fraction* is composed mainly of the ribosomes together with adhering pieces of the reticular membrane.

Ribosomes are found in all cells that synthesize protein, but the proportion attached to the endoplasmic reticular membrane varies greatly. Thus in actively secreting cells, such as those of the pancreas which produce many of the digestive enzymes, a large fraction of the ribosomes are membrane-associated. Also, in development from embryonic adult tissues, differentiation is accompanied by a shift from free to membrane-bound particles. However, in bacteria and in some protozoa, the free ribosomes make protein as well as, if not better than, ribosomes from mammalian cells.

Ribosomes isolated in magnesium-free media tend to come apart and form smaller particles unable to synthesize proteins. This dissociation, which can be reversed by increasing the magnesium ion concentration, can also be prevented by certain naturally occurring polyamines, such as spermine and spermidine. Alexander Rich, at the Massachusetts Institute of Technology, has shown that the protein "factories" of the cell are not single ribosomes working in isolation but collections of ribosomes working together in orderly fashion. These he has called polyribosomes or, more simply, *polysomes*, in which the ribosomes are held together by a strand of messenger RNA (Chap. 4).

There is evidence also that only a small proportion of the ribosomes within the cell synthesize protein at any one time, although what prevents the remainder from doing so is not known. In this respect it is of interest that during the early period of development in the chick, inactive four-ribosome polysomes, insensitive to ribonuclease (an enzyme which destroys RNA), have the form of tight symmetrical squares in feather-forming cells. Later, however, when they become sensitive to ribonuclease and can synthesize protein, the squares open up so that the four-ribosome polysomes are strung out in the configuration characteristic of functioning polysomes.

The products synthesized by ribosomes are somehow transferred to the internal vesicular spaces enclosed by membranes of the reticulum. They are then transported within this system of canals to other parts of the cell.

The endoplasmic reticulum is connected also with two other structures. First, it is continuous with a system of tightly packed, smooth-surfaced tubules, the *golgi complex,* which has been credited with the accumulation of secretory products and other macromolecules in the animal cell. Second, the endoplasmic reticulum is continuous with the double membrane surrounding the nucleus, a specialized area of protoplasm containing the genetic material of the cell. This double envelope does not completely surround the nucleus which is, therefore, connected to the rest of the cytoplasm by pores (*Fig. 1–7*).

The colloidal material which makes up the cytoplasmic matrix is capable of both viscous flow like a liquid and elastic deformation like a solid; it varies with the physiological state of the cell and the area under study. Although no obvious organized framework has been detected so far with the electron microscope, a certain degree of fibrillar structure has been demonstrated. Thus both *centrioles* which are involved in the formation of the spindle during nuclear division and *basal bodies* from which the cilia or flagella of many cells are derived show fibrillar organization. However, many primitive organisms, such as slime molds, show no organization but still can carry out rapid cytoplasmic streaming. It is possible, therefore, that special macromolecules are present to direct the organized activity of the cytoplasm.

The cytoplasmic matrix is the location of many enzyme systems including the ones concerned with fermentation or glycolysis; it also contains organelles such as mitochondria, chloroplasts (in green plants), and lysosomes, as well as the nucleus. Before the discussion of these, some remarks of A. D. McLaren and K. L. Babcock on intracellular enzymes should be considered:

> It is clear that the study of enzyme reactions in solution, although a preliminary step, cannot be expected to be sufficient for a thorough understanding of the enzymology of a living cell. Enzymology must eventually develop more closely in companionship with cell morphology. Cytochemical localizations of enzymes represent a primitive beginning in this direction; the effort must be made to correlate reaction rates with the ion-exchange properties and three-dimensional arrays of macromolecules as gels and membranes. . . . If, in the organized cell, enzymes operate as parts of structures, then a new kind of enzyme kinetic theory must be formulated. The theory must take into account the diffusion of substrate to and from the structure, or else the diffusion of the enzyme in and about the substrate structure. Very little seems to be known about these phenomena. . . . Taken all in all, we may infer that the amount of an enzyme in a structured system does not alone dictate the reaction kinetics, since the rate will depend on the structural restrictions and on the relative amounts of enzyme and substrate.[3]

The authors summarize their discussion by stating:

> Many of the enzyme reactions in nature take place on surfaces or in ordered structures. At interfaces the "concentrations" of reactants generally differ from those in solution and one such difference may be revealed by study of pH optima for enzyme reactions. In gels and at interfaces in cells the terms "concentration," "diffusion," and "pH" cannot be readily applied and must eventually be replaced by conceptually clear notions amenable to mathematical treatment before the cell physiologist can hope to deal quantitatively with the microheterogeneity of the cell.[3]

■ THE MITOCHONDRION

These subcellular organelles, which were among the first to be examined by the integrated techniques of biochemistry, cytology, and electron microscopy, are present in the cytoplasm of both plant and animal cells, including aerobic yeast cells and other lower organisms of relatively large size, such as amoebae or paramecia. They are not found in bacteria where the corresponding function is carried out by the *protoplast* membrane. Since most bacteria are only about one hundred times longer than the macromolecules of which they are composed, it would be impossible for them to contain the type of organelles found in more complex living organisms.

The size and shape of mitochondria depend to some extent on the method used to prepare them, on the physiological condition of the cell, and more particularly on cell type. In cells where they are relatively free in the cytoplasm, such as liver, kidney, and pancreas, the mitochondria are usually elongated structures; but they can exist in quite different forms, as illustrated by the large slablike mitochondria or ringlike forms that are associated with the myofibrils of insect flight muscle. In fact, in the words of Ritchie and Hazeltine:

> Mitochondria can be seen to swell, coil, branch, fragment, coalesce, put out pseudopods, even to get tied in knots. They can change their form until they resemble bubbles, strings of beads, dumb-bells, lemons or snowshoes.[4]

The number of mitochondria per cell also can vary considerably. Spermatozoa contain relatively few (about 20 per cell), mammalian liver cells may contain around 800 per cell, and certain protozoa such as the giant amoeba *chaos chaos* may contain as many as 500,000. In rat liver cells the mitochondria occupy about 20 per cent of the total cytoplasmic volume, and their half life is said to be about ten days.

A typical mitochondrion (*Fig. 1–4*) is a sausage-shaped body about 10^{-3} mm long and one-third as wide; it has an outer and inner unit membrane separated by a fluid-filled space, so that the mitochondrial structure may be visualized as a sac within a sac. The outer membrane is smooth, whereas the inner membrane has many deep infoldings, the *cristae*, which may vary considerably in conformation according to cell type.

The relation between mitochondrial structure and function has been investigated thoroughly by A. L. Lehninger and his group at the Johns Hopkins University and D. E. Green and coworkers at Wisconsin. They fragmented mitochondria into smaller and smaller units by sonication and treatment with detergents. After separating the fractions and examining them in the electron microscope, they tested them for biochemical activity. The capacity to carry out the full fatty acid oxidation and citric acid cycle reactions (Chap. 3) was lost as soon as the general form of the mitochondrion was destroyed and the matrix material allowed to leak out. However, the coupling of oxidation to the synthesis of ATP (oxidative phosphorylation) remained as long as double membranes, such as those formed by apposition of the inner and outer membranes, persisted. When the double membranes were reduced to single-membrane fragments,

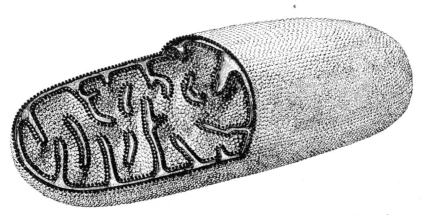

Fig. 1-4. Cutaway drawing of a typical mitochondrion shows the two membrane layers separated by a fluid-filled space called the intrastructure space. The space within the inner membrane is called the interstructure space. The invaginations of the inner membrane are the cristae. The stalkless particles distributed over the outer surface of the outer membrane are involved in various oxidation reactions that supply electrons to the interior of the mitochondrion. The particles extending inward on short stalks from the inner surface of the inner membrane transfer the electrons along a chain of complexes that synthesize molecules of adenosine triphosphate (ATP). (From D. E. Green, "The Mitochondrion." Copyright © 1964 by Scientific American, Inc. All rights reserved.)

only the ability to transport electrons remained, a function shown to be carried out by the *electron transfer particles.*

Electron transfer particles are inner-membrane, macromolecular assemblies each containing at least ten different protein species in which electrons are transferred from oxidizable substrates to molecular oxygen by a stepwise series of enzyme-catalyzed reactions (Chap. 3). The electron transfer particle can be broken down into four component complexes, but these are the smallest functional elements that can be recombined without loss of electron transfer activity. The enzymes of the citric acid cycle are easily lost during fragmentation of the mitochondria and may, therefore, be located in the liquid matrix. Green believes, however, that they are loosely associated with the inner membrane near the electron transfer particles.

Lehninger has shown that mitochondria can undergo considerable change in volume, and that this is determined by the activity of the respiratory chain and the concentration of ATP. When the latter is present in high concentrations in the cell, mitochondria extrude water, and their membranes contract, closing off the entry of energy-yielding material. When the amount of cytoplasmic ATP is low, the mitochondrial membranes expand, and their permeability increases. A number of compounds, including inorganic phosphate, fatty acids, and glutathione, as well as very low concentrations of certain hormones such as thyroxine and insulin, also can act as mitochondrial swelling agents. A contractile protein similar in many respects to the actomyosin of skeletal muscle is believed to be involved in these mitochondrial changes.

Mitochondria usually are aggregated in areas of the cell in which the demand for energy in the form of ATP is high. Thus in muscle they are found closely associated with the contractile myofibrils, in sperm arranged in helical layers surrounding the midpiece, and in nerve cells at the synapses. They also occur in large numbers immediately below the cell membrane near the base of cilia in protozoa; while in cells which are active in synthesizing protein, mitochondria are associated intimately with the ergastoplasm, where presumably they provide ATP for amino acid activation and protein synthesis on the ribosomes (Chap. 4). Also, mitochondria frequently are located near a supply of substrate and have been found wrapped around lipid droplets in cells, particularly in fasted animals. In addition, mitochondria are abundant in secretory cells such as those of the kidney tubules, and here they tend to be polarized with their long axes disposed in the direction of active secretion or transport.

Mitochondria not only are the "power plants" of the cell but also they can take up and extrude water and are involved in the transport and accumulation of certain other substances, in particular calcium, magnesium, and phosphate ions.

There is now considerable biochemical evidence that the functional parts of the mitochondrial membrane form a unitized system with structural protein. The structural and functional units are thus two facets of a single architectural design, and only a highly ordered and precisely coordinated system could carry out the multitude of coupled biochemical reactions with the high degree of efficiency observed.

Some of the many problems still to be resolved include the molecular details of oxidative phosphorylation and ion transport and the biogenesis of mitochondria. The origin of much of the protein which is unique to the mitochondrion and does not occur elsewhere in the cell also is of considerable interest, and DNA, RNA, and ribosomes have been shown to be present in these organelles.

■ **THE CHLOROPLAST**

These disk-shaped cytoplasmic structures (0.5×10^{-5} mm in diameter) are present in all green plants and contain the pigment chlorophyll by which radiant energy is trapped during photosynthesis (Chap. 3). The chloroplast (plastid) is, therefore, a cellular converter or *transducing system* (Chap. 2) that transfers radiant energy into chemical energy. As in mitochondria, a high degree of order exists in chloroplasts. They have been shown to contain layered disklike structures, the grana (*Fig. 1–5*), which are oriented membrane units containing the biochemical machinery for photosynthesis.

The functional unit in a granum is a pair of membranes called a *lamellar unit* in which chlorophyll and the yellow carotenoid pigments are arranged in monolayers, thereby achieving an enormously increased surface area for trapping light photons. Integration of structure and function in chloroplasts is indicated by the fact that chlorophyll synthesis appears to parallel lamellar unit formation; any factor which destroys the integrity of the lamellar structure also interferes with pigment formation.

The stacking pattern found in chloroplasts of higher plants is not essential for photosynthesis, since in many lower forms, like the green algae, grana are usually absent, and the lamellar units are distributed throughout the matrix of the cell. Here, however, the units are frequently elongated, often forming extensive membrane systems suggestive of end-to-end fusion of the lamellae. It is the presence of the lamellar unit that is essential for photosynthesis; the way it is arranged in the cell is of minor importance. A related phenomenon is seen in the stacked disk structure of retinal rod outer segments bearing the visual pigment rhodopsin.

There is now considerable evidence that chloroplasts and mitochondria can arise from pre-existing organelles, and that control

Fig. 1-5. Chloroplast from maize-cell. Chloroplast is the organelle in a plant cell within which photosynthesis takes place. The chlorophyll is contained in the "grana," stacks of membranous sacs called lamellae, seen here in cross section. A maize-cell chloroplast is enlarged 19,000 diameters in this electron micrograph made by A. E. Vatter of the University of Colorado Medical Center. (From E. L. Rabinowitch and Govindjee, "The Role of Chlorophyll in Photosynthesis." Copyright © 1965 by Scientific American, Inc. All rights reserved.)

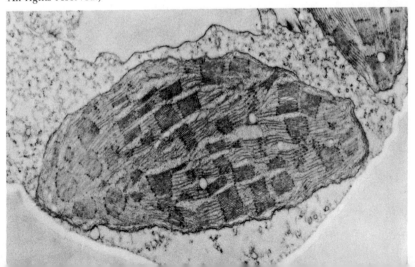

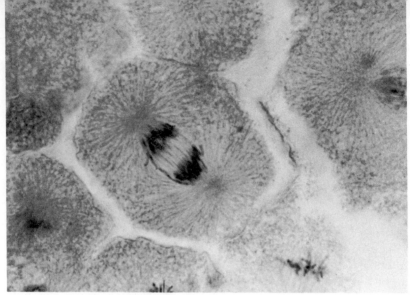

Fig. 1-6. Chromosomes in dividing cells. (From *The Cell*, Monograph of the Upjohn Company, Kalamazoo. Photo by Norman Drake.)

mechanisms (Chap. 5) exist for their differentiation. Furthermore, chloroplasts as well as mitochondria have been shown to contain DNA and RNA.

■ THE LYSOSOME

First identified in rat liver cells by C. de Duve in 1955, lysosomes are now known to occur in most animal cells, although it remains to be shown that they are present in plants. These subcellular sacs of approximately the same size as mitochondria contain a number of powerful digestive enzymes with pH optima in the acid range; in fact, they function in many ways as the digestive system of the cell. It is significant that they are particularly abundant in macrophages and white blood cells which are called on to perform important digestive tasks. They are involved in the intracellular breakdown (lysis) of macromolecules and bodies as large as bacteria which have been engulfed by the cell; they also partake in physiological *autolysis* (self-digestion). The regression of the tail of the tadpole during its metamorphosis to the adult form is accompanied by lysosomal digestion of the tail, and aged or damaged, nonfunctioning organelles may also be disposed of in this manner. In starvation, lysosomes have been shown to engulf subcellular structures such as mitochondria, presumably to feed the rest of the cell.

Lysosomes also may be involved in pathological or degenerative conditions. In a severe form of *glycogen storage disease*, for example, a lysosomal enzyme that attacks glycogen has been shown to be missing, while in anoxia, or after treatment with cellular poisons, the lysosomal membrane may rupture and release enzymes which then digest the cell and surrounding structures.

Cellular dissolution by lysosomal enzymes also occurs after death of the organism and is responsible for the process of autolysis. The lysosome, therefore, can be considered as a potential "suicide bag," and a challenging question is presented by the lysosomal unit membrane which enables the organelle to contain enzymes that on liberation are capable of digesting the entire cell. It is of interest that steroids, like cortisone, have a stabilizing influence on this membrane. This may account, at least partly, for the anti-inflammatory effect of these compounds.

■ THE NUCLEUS

The structure of the nucleus is particularly important to all biological science, because the *chromosomes* (*Fig. 1–6*) that it contains are concerned with the storage and also the transmission of hereditary characteristics (genes) of the cell. Furthermore, the nucleus is the main center for the synthesis of DNA and RNA and for the control of cytoplasmic activities.

The essential role of the nucleus between divisions can be demonstrated by experiments involving the removal and transplantation of this structure. Both enucleated cells and cells with nuclei that have been damaged by irradiation regress and die; but if a nucleus from the same species is implanted soon after enucleation, the cell becomes reactivated and may even divide to produce a mass culture. On the other hand, cytoplasmic fragments from the giant alga *Acetabularia* can survive several months without a nucleus and are capable of limited growth and differentiation. Therefore, many of the activities of the cell, including the synthesis of protein and specific enzymes, can proceed, for a while at least, in the total absence of nuclear control. This also applies to mammalian reticulocytes which are devoid of nuclei and yet can still actively synthesize hemoglobin and differentiate into erythrocytes.

These and other experiments (Chap. 4) have shown that the nucleus produces something that is formed under the influence of DNA and is transferred then to the cytoplasm where it is used up. This product is now known to be *messenger RNA* (mRNA); but in *Acetabularia* and reticulocytes, it must be far more stable than in many other organisms, especially bacteria. Electron microscopy has demonstrated what appears to be the streaming of macromolecules into the cytoplasm through the pores of the fenestrated double membrane surrounding the nucleus (*Fig. 1–7*). It is not quite clear, however,

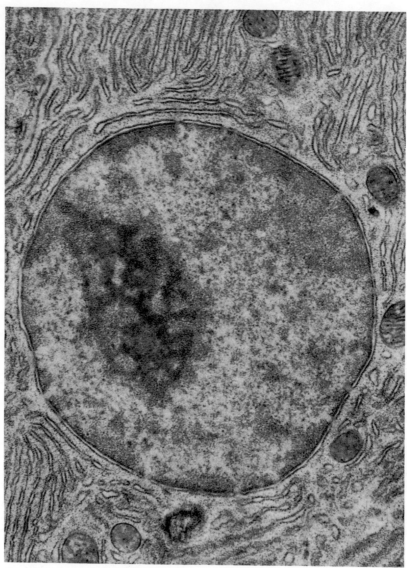

Fig. 1-7. Nucleus of the living cell is the large round object in the center of the electron micrograph on this page. The membrane around the nucleus is interrupted by pores through which the nucleus possibly communicates with the surrounding cytoplasm. The smaller round objects in the cytoplasm are mitochondria; the long, thin structures are the endoplasmic reticulum; the dark dots lining the reticulum are ribosomes. Actually the micrograph shows not a living cell but a dead cell: the cell has been fixed with a compound of the heavy metal osmium, immersed in a liquid plastic that is then made to solidify and finally sliced with a glass knife. The electron beam of the microscope mainly detects the atoms of osmium, distributed according to the affinity of the fixing compound for various cell constituents. The micrograph was made by Don W. Fawcett of the Harvard Medical School. The enlargement is 28,400 diameters. The cell itself is from the pancreas of a bat. (From J. Brachet, "The Living Cell." Copyright © 1961 by Scientific American, Inc. All rights reserved.)

whether the assembly of mRNA and ribosomes to form the active polysomes takes place in the nucleus or in the cytoplasm. The material passing through the holes in the nuclear membrane could either be mRNA bound to ribosomes or the free mRNA molecules. Certainly in the nondividing nucleus, bodies that contain granules of approximately the same size and appearance as ribosomes are known to be present. These are the *nucleoli*, and they are especially rich in RNA. The nucleus also contains a basic protein, a histone, which is complexed with DNA and may act as a regulator by suppressing the action of the nucleic acid (Chap. 5). Chromosomes, in addition, contain an acidic protein (residual protein) which varies greatly from cell to cell, being present in larger amounts in the more active tissues.

Problems of subcellular transport are less important in bacteria, since they do not possess well-defined membrane-bound nuclei but only areas rich in DNA which can be equated functionally with the nucleus of other cell types. In addition, because they lack chromosomes, bacteria do not perform the intricate choreography of mitosis at cell division.

In recent years elegant experiments by R. Briggs and T. J. King have shown that cell nuclei taken from late embryonic stages are not equivalent to the nucleus of the frog egg cell from which they were derived. They will no longer give rise to normal embryos if transplanted into enucleated eggs; the kind of abnormality observed also depends on the part of the embryo from which the nucleus was taken. This indicates that changes within the nucleus are occurring during development (see also Vol. IV).

Chapter 1 has examined most of the functional components of the cell, but the material presented provides one with very little information about how cells differentiate and interact to form the specialized tissues and organs of more complex organisms. In the words of W. S. Beck:

Living organisms are not nucleic acid, however, and we must make a real effort to bear this in mind. Though we have spoken chiefly of the gene and the enzyme, it is the organism that lives in the world, that walks and grows and writes books on biology. What is the nature of this complexity that knows so many forms, but fails to hide their brotherhood? What is there about the organism that has made poets sing and scientists despair?

The essence of organism is at once subtle and irresistibly fascinating. The secret is in its name. The organism is an *organization* of materials and functions that are dedicated to the preservation of itself and its species. The allure of this concept, however, stems from the intricate system of levels of organization, a pattern which characterizes all living things. Thus, the cell is an organized entity at one level of complexity. It lives in a community of other cells, joining them in certain projects, competing with them for food, and either dying or dividing to form new offspring. Yet these cells may be part of a higher organization, the brain, which is a whole made up of the sum of its parts. Here is a structure on a more complex level of organization, existing and interacting in a community of other organs, not cells. Likewise, the whole man is still higher on the scale of organization, and men talk to other men, not brains or cells. We may also start with the cell and go down the ladder, for within the cell are self-concerned substructures like the nucleus, the particles within the nucleus, and the particles within those particles—until we reach the level of the molecule and atom. It is this rising table of organization that is characteristic of organism, the elusive hierarchy that makes of thin voices mighty antiphonal choirs.[5]

Many questions can be asked but few answered, and the phenomena of differentiation, growth, and morphogenesis still presents one of the most fundamental and fascinating problems of biology (Chap. 5 and see also Vol. IV).

■ VIRUSES

It has been established that cells are complex membrane-bound macromolecular assemblies endowed with the properties of life. A group of particles, the *viruses*, falls into an intermediate category between the living and the nonliving. They are macromolecules which gain the attribute of life only in conjunction with the host cell.

Viruses constitute a large group of highly infective agents responsible for a number of well-known diseases such as measles, mumps, chickenpox, poliomyelitis, and the common cold. They are also the cause of many plant diseases; and certain viruses, the *bacteriophages*, will attack bacteria.

Viruses are elusive "creatures" small enough to pass through bacterial filters and visible only in the electron microscope. They are entirely dependent on the metabolism of their host and, therefore, cannot be grown in artificial culture media. They have neither energy metabolism nor enzymes for the biosynthesis of their own substance; in many ways they resemble genes. Thus in host cells they replicate identically, they express some characteristic—the symptoms of the disease—and they may undergo mutation. In addition, they contain nucleic acid which carries the information for their own specificity and directs the host cell to form virus-specific substances. In this process the viral genome becomes part of the host chromosome. Furthermore, bacteriophages can carry genes from one bacterium to another (transduction) and thus may produce a genetically altered strain. Genetic alteration produced by purified chromosomal DNA is known as *transformation* (see also Vol. III).

The long thread of nucleic acid in viruses is embedded in protein and generally consists of DNA, although in a number of plant and some animal viruses it is RNA. In addition, the DNA of some small bacterial viruses such as ΦX 174 is not in the double-stranded Watson-Crick configuration (see Vol. I) but instead is composed of only a single, polynucleotide strand which is probably cyclic in structure. The simplest virus known contains nucleic acid composed of only about 1000 nucleotide units, just enough to code for an average size protein (Chap. 4). However, it is never found alone but only in cells that are simultaneously infected with a larger virus.

Many viruses have now been obtained in pure form and some, like the tobacco mosaic virus, even have been crystallized. They consist only of nucleic acid surrounded by a protein overcoat which accounts for 95 per cent of the total weight.

The structure of bacteriophages is a little more elaborate, however; and their study has contributed much to molecular genetics (see Vol. III). A typical T-even phage particle (*Fig. 1–8*) consists of a head region and a tail assembled from at least four different protein components: a sheath, a core, a base plate, and six fibers. The tail fibers are used specifically to anchor the virus to the phage-sensitive bacterium, and the base plate also may be used for this purpose. The sheath protein is contractile and can force the tail core DNA toward the interior of the host cell rather like a hypodermic syringe whose needle is pushed under the skin by release of a built-in spring.

The penetration of only the viral DNA was demonstrated beautifully by Alfred D. Hershey and Martha C. Chase in a classic experiment using T2 phage, with its coat protein labeled with radioactive sulfur (^{35}S) and its DNA core labeled with radioactive phosphorus (^{32}P). After infecting a culture of *E. coli* with the bacteriophage, the bacterial suspension was agitated violently in a Waring blender; this removed nearly all the ^{35}S but virtually none of the ^{32}P. It was inferred, therefore, from these and other experiments that most of the phage DNA enters the bacterium during infection, whereas most of the protein remains at the cell surface. However, as noted by G. S. Stent, several problems are raised by these findings:

> How does the single, enormous viral DNA macromolecule travel from the phage head into the interior of the host cell? . . . Since the width of the hole in the sheath is little larger than the 20 Å diameter of the DNA molecules themselves, the DNA would have to pass through the sheath as a single thread. The nature of the moving force of this process, whose dynamics would be roughly equivalent to quickly pushing a 10-meter length of string 1 mm thick through a narrow straw, is less clear. In any case, the energy-yielding reaction of the host cell does not seem to be called upon for this purpose,

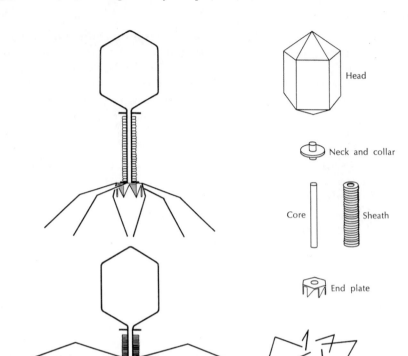

Head

Neck and collar

Core   Sheath

End plate

Fibers

Cell wall

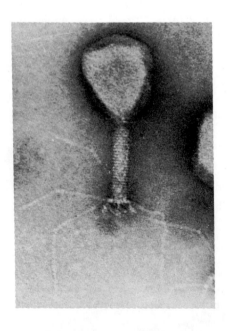

Fig. 1-8. Structure of a virus. (left) T4 bacteriophage is enlarged about 300,000 diameters in an electron micrograph made by Michael Moody of the California Institute of Technology. The preparation was negatively stained with electron-dense uranyl acetate, which makes the background dark. (above) T4 components are diagrammed. A complete virus particle is shown at top left. Below it is a particle attached to a bacterial cell wall, with its sheath contracted and its hollow core penetrating the cell wall. The various components are shown separately at the right. (Courtesy Dr. M. F. Moody of the Rockefeller Institute; from R. S. Edgar and R. H. Epstein, "Genetics of a Bacterial Virus." Copyright © 1965 by Scientific American, Inc. All rights reserved.)

since the DNA is ejected from the phage head after adsorption to either heat-killed bacteria or isolated cell walls or after various chemical and physical treatments of the free phage particles. One may imagine, therefore, that the DNA is packed in the phage head under constraint and forces its own way through the sheath after the contraction and "uncorking" reactions of the tail are triggered.[6]

1. From "The Membrane of the Living Cell" by J. David Robertson, *Scientific American*, Vol. 206, April 1962, p. 65. Copyright © 1962 by Scientific American, Inc. All rights reserved.
2. D. E. Green and O. Hechter, "Assembly of Membrane Subunits," *Proceedings of the National Academy of Sciences*, 53 (1965), 318.
3. A. D. McLaren and K. L. Babcock, "Some Characteristics of Enzyme Reactions at Surfaces," in *Subcellular Particles*, ed. Teru Hayashi. The Ronald Press Company, New York, 1959, pp. 23–36.
4. Ritchie and Hazeltine, in D. Haldar, K. Freeman, and T. S. Work, "Biogenesis of Mitochondria," *Nature*, 211 (1966), 9.
5. William S. Beck, *Modern Science and the Nature of Life*, by permission of Harcourt, Brace, and World, Inc., New York, and Macmillan & Company, Ltd., London, 1957, pp. 254–255.
6. From *Molecular Biology of Bacterial Viruses* by Gunther S. Stent, W. H. Freeman and Company, San Francisco. Copyright 1963, p. 113.

CHAPTER 2 The Dynamic
State of
Biological Systems

■ LIFE AND THE STEADY STATE

Life is a steady state in which free energy* must be continuously liberated to maintain the viability of cells of an organism. What is meant by "steady state"?

It has been stressed already that the macromolecular components of the cell (proteins, nucleic acids, and polysaccharides) are very precisely ordered molecules which are themselves part of an ordered structure. Since it is a basic principle of physics (the second law of thermodynamics†) that a system when left to itself tends to decrease its state of orderliness unless free energy is supplied, the need for a constant source of energy becomes apparent. As soon as the supply of energy is cut off, living systems become disorganized, that is, they die; and this type of labile system that is maintained at a certain level of organization only by the continuous expenditure of work is known as a *steady state*. It should not be confused with chemical equilibrium in which the system is at its lowest free energy level and in a state of maximum disorder. It is necessary, therefore, to apply thermodynamics to the steady state condition in biological systems rather than to the equilibrium conditions for which thermodynamics was first developed. In addition, the chemical reactions within living systems occur in heterogeneous systems involving more than one phase and

---

* Free energy is that component of the total energy of a system which can do work under isothermal conditions.

† Thermodynamics is the branch of physics that deals with energy and its transformations.

so further complicate any calculations based on classical thermo-dynamics. These considerations, therefore, must always be kept in mind when trying to extend results obtained using purified enzymes to the situation in the intact organism.

The second law of thermodynamics has been aptly described by Beck:

> . . . it states that the negative entropy of a system, which is, among other things, a measure of its degree of molecular order, is always moving in the direction of chaos, and, in any self-contained corner of the universe, order may be restored only by putting energy into the system. To anyone with a formal garden these physical terms are unnecessary. If the garden is planted in a highly ordered arrangement of rows and designs, energy must be expended constantly to prevent any drift towards disorder in the form of weeds, ragged growth, and desiccation.[1]

The concept of a dynamic steady state of all tissue components is fundamental to both biology and biochemistry and was emphasized in the work of Schoenheimer and his collaborators. In his classical monograph, *The Dynamic State of Body Constituents*, R. Schoenheimer wrote:

> The large molecules such as the fats and the proteins are under the influence of lytic enzymes, constantly being degraded to their constituent fragments. These changes are balanced by synthetic processes which must be coupled to other chemical reactions such as oxidation and dephosphorylation. After death, when the oxidative systems disappear, the synthetic processes also cease, and the unbalanced degradative reactions lead to the collapse of the thermodynamically unstable structural elements. In general, every regeneration reaction involving an increase in free energy must be coupled with another process. In order to maintain structure against its tendency to collapse, work has to be done. The replacement of a brick fallen from a wall requires energy, and in the living organism energy debts are paid by chemical reactions.
>
> For the few coupled biochemical reactions which have been carefully investigated, such as those involved in muscle contraction or respiration, it has been shown that every chemical step is specifically related to some other one. The complex organic molecules present in living matter must require for their maintenance the steady occurrence of various reactions. The finding of the rapid molecular regeneration, involving constant transfer of specific groups, suggests that the biological system represents one great cycle of closely linked chemical reactions. This idea can scarcely be reconciled with the classical comparison of the living being to a combustion engine nor with the theory of independent exogenous and endogenous types of

metabolism. The simile of the combustion engine pictured the steady flow of fuel into a fixed system, and the conversion of this fuel into waste products. The new results imply that not only the fuel but the structural materials are in a steady state of flow. The classical picture must be replaced by one which takes account of the dynamic state of body structure.[2]

A balance, therefore, is struck between the synthesis and breakdown of the complex materials of the cell substances and their specific constituents, and the equilibrium that exists in this dynamic system is due to synthesis and breakdown proceeding simultaneously at equal rates. In the words of H. A. Krebs:

> From the chemical point of view living matter can be described as a system of innumerable reactions which form, to quote Hopkins, a "dynamic equilibrium." The term "equilibrium" expresses the fact that in spite of numerous and often rapid chemical changes, living material has a fairly constant chemical composition. Pieces of liver or brain, for example, taken from the same organism at, say, monthly or yearly intervals are found to be virtually identical in their chemical composition. The term "dynamic" indicates that the constancy is an apparent one. It is the result of numerous counterbalancing reactions. How fast some of these reactions are may be gathered from the fact that the oxygen uptake of liver or brain would be sufficiently rapid to burn all organic matter in the tissue within less than three days if no replacement took place.
>
> Living matter becomes dead matter when the balance of chemical reactions is deranged beyond certain limits. In most tissues of higher organisms the elimination of *one* reaction—that concerned with the uptake of molecular oxygen—will within a few minutes (in the case of the brain) or within a few hours (in the case of muscle or liver) so upset the dynamic equilibrium that all chemical activities come to a standstill. The dynamic system becomes static. . . . How is the "dynamic equilibrium" maintained? It has been said that two different types of reactions can be distinguished in the tangle of processes making up the "dynamic equilibrium": (1) truly reversible reactions which oscillate around an equilibrium point according to the change of conditions; (2) irreversible reactions which temporarily upset the equilibrium of reversible reactions.
>
> In a system like living matter where temperature and concentration of reactants vary relatively little, the change of free energy of truly reversible reactions is usually very small. Truly reversible reactions, therefore, have little scope for producing work of any kind, be it mechanical work in muscle or chemical synthesis in glands or growing cells, or the osmotic work of excretion and absorption. Truly reversible reactions cannot result in any major changes within living matter; therefore they lead nowhere. They merely protect, within limits, a certain set of conditions against the influence of changing circumstances. They are "buffers" in the wider sense of the word.

Just as pH buffers keep the concentration of H and OH − ions within certain limits, so other truly reversible systems maintain, again within limits, a certain constancy of conditions. The chief manifestations of life − movement, synthesis, growth − all depend primarily on irreversible processes. Thus living matter is faced with the problem of maintaining a relative constancy of its chemical composition in spite of very rapid irreversible processes.[3]

It must be borne in mind, however, that living matter not only is constantly replacing components that have become altered during their function but also is extending itself by growth and duplication.

Still on the theme of thermodynamics, the first law states that energy can neither be created nor destroyed but merely is converted from one form to another. Certainly this applies to living systems, and the total energy liberated when a given amount of material is completely oxidized is the same whether this occurs by a series of enzyme-catalyzed reactions in a living organism or by direct combustion in a test tube.

■ ENERGY-RICH COMPOUNDS

When a substance is broken down in the cell, usually by oxidation, all the free energy obtainable is not liberated at once. Instead, it is tapped off in stages, and, if not required immediately, it can be stored in various ways. The free energy can be trapped through the formation of certain compounds of which one in particular, adenosine triphosphate (ATP), is universally distributed in living matter and plays a fundamental role in energy exchange reactions.

Adenosine triphosphate (ATP)

It is called a "high-energy" or "energy-rich" compound, because the removal of its terminal phosphate radical by hydrolysis is accompanied by a large decrease in free energy (about 9000 calories per gram molecule). The reaction is said to be *exergonic*.

$$A—\circled{P}—\circled{P}—\circled{P} + H_2O \longrightarrow A—\circled{P}—\circled{P} + HO\circled{P}; \Delta F = -9000 \text{ cal}$$

The hydrolysis of adenosine diphosphate (ADP) to adenosine monophosphate (AMP) also results in a large decrease in free energy; but the third phosphate group, which is linked by an ester linkage instead of a pyrophosphate bond, yields relatively little energy. To this last group belong the various sugar phosphate esters which act as intermediates in fermentation and glycolysis (Chap. 3).

Other types of naturally occurring, high-energy compounds include acetyl and carbamyl phosphate, phosphoenol pyruvate, arginine and creatine phosphate, and acetyl coenzyme A.

$$\overset{\overset{\text{O}}{\|}}{CH_3—C—O—\circled{P}} \qquad \overset{\overset{\text{O}}{\|}}{H_2N—C—O—\circled{P}}$$

Acetyl phosphate   **Carbamyl phosphate**

$$\begin{array}{c} \text{COOH} \\ | \\ \text{C—O—}\circled{P} \\ \| \\ \text{CH}_2 \end{array}$$

Phosphoenol pyruvate

$$\underset{\underset{\text{CH}_3}{|}}{\text{HOOC—N—}\overset{\overset{\text{NH}}{\|}}{C}\text{—NH—}\circled{P}} \qquad \overset{\overset{\text{O}}{\|}}{CH_3—C—SCoA}$$

Creatine phosphate   **Acetyl coenzyme A**

The energy-rich nature of these substances is believed to be due to differences in the resonance stabilities, ionizations, and intramolecular electrostatic repulsions of the compounds and their products of hydrolysis. This is beautifully explained by Lehninger:

> There are two basic features of the ATP molecule which endow it with a relatively high free energy of hydrolysis; both are properties of the highly charged polyphosphate structure. At pH 7.0 the linear polyphosphate structure of ATP has four negative charges which are very close to each other and which repel each other very strongly.

When the terminal phosphate bond is hydrolyzed, some of this electrostatic stress is relieved; the similar charges are separated as the ADP^{3-} and phosphate^{2-} ions. Once they are separated, they will tend to stay as far away from each other as possible and will have very little tendency to approach each other again because of the electrostatic repulsion. In contrast, simple low-energy phosphate esters of alcohols, for example, have no such repulsion forces at pH 7.0 between the products of hydrolysis because one of these, the alcohol R—OH, has no charge at all.

$$R—O—\overset{\overset{\displaystyle O^-}{|}}{\underset{\underset{\displaystyle O}{\|}}{P}}—O^- + H_2O \rightleftarrows R—OH + HO—\overset{\overset{\displaystyle O^-}{|}}{\underset{\underset{\displaystyle O}{\|}}{P}}—O^-$$

The second major factor contributing to the relatively high free energy of hydrolysis of ATP is the fact that the two products ADP and phosphate undergo stabilization as *resonance hybrids* as soon as they are formed. As it happens, the electrons around the P and O atoms of ATP, ADP, and phosphate may in each case be arranged in several different ways, but they tend always to seek the arrangement having the lowest possible energy level. Because of this tendency, the energy content of the two reaction products, ADP and phosphate, once they are separated from each other, is considerably lower than these two structures possessed when they were still part of the ATP molecule. When the bond was broken a new arrangement of their electrons was made possible, one having a much lower energy content. Such resonance stabilization of the hydrolysis products is a major reason for the relatively high free energy of hydrolysis of this class of phosphate esters.[4]

The practice in biochemistry of referring to high-energy and low-energy "*bonds*," although useful for illustrative purposes, is erroneous because it implies that the energy is concentrated in a single chemical bond. In fact, it depends on the structure of both the compound and its product and also on the type of chemical reaction involved, namely hydrolysis.

ATP is the immediate source of energy for a great number of biological systems. Various types of work which utilize high-energy phosphate are shown in *Fig. 2–1*. The cellular structural devices that transform energy from one form to another are known as *transducing systems*.

In many reactions ATP can act as a phosphorylating agent, transferring inorganic phosphate to glucose, for example, to form glucose-6-phosphate. This reaction is of fundamental importance in carbohydrate metabolism, because glucose is generally phosphorylated before it is broken down further or converted to polysaccharides. The

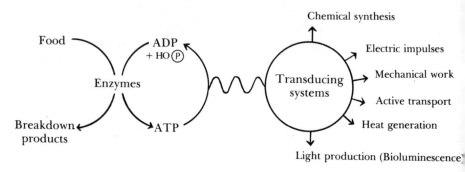

Fig. 2–1. The role of ATP in energy transfer.

ADP that is generated can be reconverted to ATP by general metabolic reactions or, in muscle, from other energy-rich compounds, such as arginine or creatine phosphate, also known as *phosphagens*.

$$\text{ADP} + \text{Creatine phosphate} \underset{\text{Kinase}}{\overset{\text{Creatine}}{\rightleftharpoons}} \text{Creatine} + \text{ATP}$$

Since this last reaction, named after its discoverer Lohmann, is freely reversible and results in very little energy change, the phosphagens act as a readily available source of high energy, particularly during intense muscular activity.

In some cases, as in the activation of amino acids for protein synthesis or in the formation of the acetyl coenzyme A derivatives of fatty acids (Chap. 4), ATP is broken down to AMP and pyrophosphate. The latter compound is also formed when ATP and related nucleoside triphosphates or their deoxy derivatives give rise to RNA and DNA respectively. In addition, other nucleoside diphosphates containing guanine, cytosine, or uracil can be phosphorylated by ATP to yield the corresponding triphosphates which are then utilized for specific synthetic reactions (Chap. 4). Thus cytidine triphosphate (CTP) is involved in phospholipid synthesis, uridine triphosphate (UTP) in glycogen formation, and guanosine triphosphate (GTP) in protein synthesis. However, the ultimate energy requirements of the cell are provided by ATP which thus acts as a messenger between *exergonic* reactions, or those that supply energy, and *endergonic* reactions, or those that utilize it.

■ **TRANSDUCING SYSTEMS**

When ATP is broken down in muscle, the free energy liberated appears largely in the form of muscular contraction. The protein, *myosin*, which is itself a constituent of the contractile machinery of the muscle cell, plays the part of a "transformer" or transducing system which converts chemical into mechanical energy.

In the electric organs of certain fishes such as the electric ray, *torpedo*, transducing systems of a different kind are present. Myosin is lacking in the most highly developed of these organs, but the electrical energy that they show arises from ATP, as does the light energy dissipated by bioluminescent organisms such as the firefly. In fact, the intensity of light emitted when ATP is added to an extract of firefly tails has been found to be proportional to the amount of ATP present and can be used to assay this nucleotide. Bioluminescence is frequently described as "cold light," because it is a highly efficient energy-transfer process with very little dissipation of heat; the intensity of light produced can be considerable (*Fig. 2–2*).

Transducing systems as a class and the correlation between structure and function have been aptly discussed by D. E. Green and S. Fleischer:

> Living systems contain a variety of structured devices or machines that transform energy from one form to another — radiant to chemical energy, chemical to mechanical energy, chemical to radiant energy, etc. These devices known as *transducing systems* are fundamental to the work performance of living cells and without such devices all cellular activity would be impossible. Any physiological process such as transmission of a nerve impulse, muscular contraction or vision may involve the close collaboration of several machines, e.g., the

Fig. 2-2. The light from this photograph was provided by dehydrated firefly tails. (From Schwarz BioResearch, Inc., Orangeberg, New York.)

mitochondrion and the membrane apparatus in nerve transmission; the mitochondrion and the myofibril in muscular contraction; and the mitochondrion with elements of the retinal rods, retinal cones and nerve cells in vision.

Transducing systems as a class have several properties in common. They are all contained within subcellular particles or membranes of highly intricate structure. They do not occur singly but rather in clusters or large numbers of repeating units that are embedded in some structured medium. In general those systems contain a high proportion of lipid and exhibit double membraned (lamellar) structure.

The transduction is a molecular process that is consummated by the cyclical performance of specialized transducing compounds, and the organized structure of the transducing systems is designed or hand-tailored as if it were for the performance of these specialized molecules. Chlorophyll in the photosynthesizing chloroplasts, luciferin in the luminescent organ of the firefly, rhodopsin in the retinal cones and rods and myosin and actin in the myofibrils are among the well-documented transducing molecules. The key to transduction is clearly the mode of action of these transducing molecules but it must be remembered that only in the context of the organized system can the action of these molecules be properly studied. Structure and function are so inextricably bound together that loss of one inevitably leads to the loss of the other. The cycle of events involving the absorption of photons by chlorophyll and the transmission of electrons to other components of the electron transport chain requires the structured milieu of the chloroplast and when this structured system is modified beyond the point of no return, chlorophyll no longer can function in precisely the same catalytic fashion as it does under physiological conditions.

The complexity of the structure-function relationship, the difficulties of working with particulates, and various other technical factors have raised formidable barriers to the study of transducing systems. Until very recently these basic systems were assiduously avoided by biochemists.[5]

■ INTERMEDIARY METABOLISM

The term *metabolism* or *intermediary metabolism* refers to the sum total of chemical processes that occur within living organisms. It can be considered to consist of two parts—*catabolism* which involves the chemical degradation of complex materials into smaller products and *anabolism* which embraces all synthetic reactions. The biosynthesis of protein from amino acids is, therefore, an anabolic process, whereas the breakdown of glucose or fat to carbon dioxide and water are catabolic processes; the products formed during these changes are known as *metabolites*. In many cases, however, the distinction between anabolism and catabolism is meaningless, either because there is no change in the size of the molecules in the reaction, or because during the breakdown sequence there is a temporary increase in the size of the substances involved. As mentioned before, synthetic and degradative processes occur simultaneously and are often *coupled,* so that energy derived from one can "drive" the other. High-energy intermediates are formed during these reactions.

Many techniques have been applied to the study of metabolism, and all such investigations may be divided into two main groups: those carried out on the whole living organism, known as *in vivo* experiments; and those in which isolated living organs and tissues, subcellular fractions, and enzyme preparations are used, known as *in vitro* experiments.

For *in vivo* experiments only animals of certain types are convenient for laboratory purposes; the majority of such investigations are carried out on rats, mice, guinea pigs, or rabbits. These animals are relatively small and breed well under laboratory conditions. They also have a rapid rate of growth and development with a moderately short life span which makes it possible to develop highly inbred strains. Since mammals have been used so commonly, the results of these experiments often apply to man; however, many exceptions are known. Thus, ascorbic acid (vitamin C) has been found to be an essential dietary component for man, apes, and guinea pigs but can be synthesized by all other species studied.

Much of our knowledge of metabolism is based also on the results of experiments with birds, insects, protozoa, bacteria, and fungi; and *comparative biochemistry,* or the study of the biochemical similarities and differences in the various divisions of the animal and plant kingdoms, is fundamental to biology.

Nature, fortunately, is relatively sparing in chemical machinery, and, although living things can exist in a whole variety of shapes and sizes, the scope of their biochemical behavior is more limited. In fact, if no broad metabolic generalizations were possible, the task of the biochemist would be virtually hopeless; and this biochemical uniformity provides good evidence for a single origin of life.

■ STUDIES ON THE WHOLE ORGANISM

In vivo experiments using whole animals or plants with their highly organized structures present many problems of interpretation, chiefly because many processes are occurring simultaneously. In addition, little information can generally be obtained about the intermediates in a complex, metabolic sequence, because these metabolites are converted rapidly to end products. It is often necessary to interrupt the normal processes in some way to encourage the formation and accumulation of intermediary substances. On the other hand, in the intact organism the constituent substrates and enzymes bear definite geometrical and chemical relationships to each other and are still under full hormonal control. The rates of reaction will also differ from the *in vitro* situation, because the various membranes of the organism serve to compartmentalize materials and to limit the rates at which substrates enter or leave certain compartments.

In animals the chief method of studying metabolism is to administer the compound under investigation by feeding or injection and then examine tissues and excreta for possible metabolic products. Obviously certain precautions are necessary. If urine is collected, care must be taken to prevent bacterial contamination. This problem is still more acute with feces, since before being voided these will have been incubated for some hours in the presence of a massive bacterial population.

The method described above has been used to study the metabolism of many, normal, dietary constituents in animals and the fate of many compounds that are foreign to the body, such as drugs and poisons. Generally, though not always, these foreign substances are rendered less harmful (detoxified) by enzymes of living tissues.

Animals that are intact but suffering from some pathological derangement of metabolism also have provided biochemical information. The abnormal metabolic condition may have occurred spontaneously, or it may have been induced experimentally. Thus spontaneous sugar diabetes, or diabetes caused by removal of the pancreas or treatment with the drug, alloxan, have been used to study the metabolism of carbohydrates, fats, and proteins. *Inborn errors of metabolism* such as albinism, for example, also have provided ways of investigating metabolic processes; and bacterial mutants have been singularly useful in elucidating biosynthetic pathways.

Removal of the liver or its surgical bypassing (Eck's fistula) can yield information about the importance of this organ in the synthesis of urea (uric acid in birds) from ammonia during amino acid metabolism (Chap. 3). Under these circumstances the concentration of amino acids and ammonia in blood and urine is greatly increased, and the formation of urea (or uric acid) virtually ceases.

A more direct way of determining which particular organ of an animal is responsible for a given biochemical change is to circulate the substance to be studied through the organ which either can be left *in situ* or removed and maintained in blood serum or in an artificial medium. Such perfusion experiments have yielded useful metabolic data and have shown, for example, that the adrenal gland can produce many different steroid hormones, and that the liver can convert pyruvic acid to the amino acid alanine. Quantitative data, however, must be interpreted with caution, as it is difficult to be certain that the whole organ is being perfused; parts of it may be dead or moribund. The hormonal environment and also other conditions probably will be abnormal.

■ STUDIES ON TISSUE SLICES AND CELL-FREE SYSTEMS

The next level of organization is the sliced organ which affords a simple and convenient way of studying metabolism. Thin tissue slices in a physiological medium will remain alive for several hours and can be used to determine whether certain substances are metabolized by the tissues under investigation. The rates of metabolism usually can be calculated from the oxygen uptake (respiration) using a Warburg manometer (see Vol. VIII); this method is also applicable to cell suspensions.

In recent years, however, the use of cell-free systems and sub-cellular particles for metabolic studies has found wide favor. In this method tissues are minced in some type of homogenizer; and various particulate structures of the cell, such as the nuclei, mitochondria, or the microsomes, are isolated by differential centrifugation (see Vol. VIII). By the addition of suitable substrates, the presence or absence of a given enzymatic activity in these subcellular fractions can be determined. Thus the mitochondria have been shown to contain the enzymes involved in cellular respiration and oxidative phosphorylation, while the chloroplasts of green plants have been shown to contain most of the enzymes needed for carbon dioxide fixation (Chap. 3).

Finally, purified enzymes extracted from the cells can be used to study metabolism, and the kinetic and thermodynamic characteristics of a particular metabolic reaction in a reaction sequence can then be established. Certain enzymes, however, are firmly bound to insoluble cellular particles and can be dissociated from them only with difficulty. Rigorous purification is essential since enzymes, like proteins in general, may form mixed crystals when still far from being chemically pure.

In working with purified enzymes, it must be remembered always that in the intact organism enzymes do not exist by themselves in a pure state, and they are subject to regulatory influences. Furthermore, since the metabolites are constantly removed, the reactions that occur inside the normal cell may never reach the equilibria attained by purified enzyme systems. Many enzymes also may have different properties in aqueous solutions than in their native lipid-rich environment.

■ STUDIES WITH TISSUE CULTURE AND MICROORGANISMS

Under favorable conditions isolated cells or tissues can be made to grow and divide *in vitro*. This process can go on almost indefinitely, if bacterial contamination is avoided.

Studies with tissue culture, using homologous cell populations to provide greater experimental uniformity and reproducibility, have provided useful information about the metabolism of resting or proliferating cells under rigidly controlled conditions. Tissue culture techniques have also been used to study the mechanism of virus propagation in cells, making it possible to examine chemical alterations induced in the host cells *in vitro* by the viral agent.

Much work on photosynthesis has been carried out with suspension of single-celled algae like *Chlorella*; this system has been adopted by Calvin and others to elucidate the series of reactions whereby plants convert carbon dioxide to carbohydrates and other organic compounds.

Microorganisms too have been used extensively to study metabolic reactions. These primitive forms which have relatively simple requirements for growth and development readily undergo mutation on irradiation with ultraviolet light or X rays. Many such mutant strains are unable to grow unless certain compounds are added to the medium, indicating that they have lost the ability to synthesize one or more substances. In every instance it has been shown that a single gene (Chap. 5) controlled the formation of a single enzyme. The early work which led to this "one gene one enzyme" hypothesis was carried out by G. W. Beadle and E. L. Tatum with the bread mold, *Neurospora crassa*.

Microorganisms have been used also in biochemical genetics to investigate bacterial transformation by preparations of DNA (see Vol. III) and to study adaptive enzyme formation in response to certain metabolites (Chap. 5).

■ ISOTOPES IN THE STUDY OF INTERMEDIARY METABOLISM

The experiments described so far have suffered from one disadvantage or another. It is often impossible to identify the intermediate products of a normal dietary substance in the intact organism, because they are indistinguishable from molecules of the same substance already present in the tissues. On the other hand, if either the organism or the test compound is abnormal, it is difficult to assess whether the results would have been the same under normal conditions. Most of these difficulties have been overcome by "labeling" or "tagging" molecules with isotopes* in order to follow their fate during metabolic transformation, and this *tracer* technique has

---

*Isotopes are atoms of elements having the same atomic number but different atomic weights. Some isotopes are radioactive because they possess unstable nuclei which decompose spontaneously emitting radiation and particles of various types. Methods for detecting isotopes are discussed in Vol. VIII of this series.

revolutionized the investigation of intermediary metabolism. These points were emphasized by Schoenheimer, one of the earliest research workers to make extensive use of isotopes in biochemical studies:

> Most of our knowledge of intermediary metabolism·is the result of balance experimentation which can give little insight into the nature and extent of chemical reactions that may conceivably take place between body constituents but do not give rise to metabolic end-products. Many attempts have been made to circumvent the fundamental difficulties by introducing readily detectable chemical labels into substances under investigation. For instance, in order to follow the metabolism of a fatty acid, one or more hydrogen atoms have been replaced by halogen. The physical and chemical properties of the compounds are, however, greatly affected by such substitution, and the highly sensitive cells or organs of the animal body cannot be expected to treat both substances alike.
>
> In order to mark a compound for biological studies the label has to be of such nature that no change of physiological properties is effected by its introduction, but the experimenter must be able to estimate it in small amounts. Labels that satisfactorily fulfill these requirements are isotopes of elements that occur in organic matter; namely, the less abundant isotopes of carbon, hydrogen, oxygen and nitrogen.

The fact that the biologist is in a position to mark organic molecules with isotopes is mainly due to the work of Urey, who not only discovered heavy hydrogen but devised methods for its large-scale concentration and that of the less abundant natural isotopes of carbon, nitrogen, oxygen and sulfur.

While Urey was making available these stable natural isotopes, radioactive elements obtained by nuclear reactions have been offered to the biologist. Within the period of a few years radioactive isotopes of almost all elements have been produced; indeed some exist in several radioactive varieties.

The living organism does not discriminate between isotopes of the same element, stable or radioactive, and treats all alike.

The first investigator to realize the practical value of these tools was Hevesy, who as early as 1923, when neither stable nor artificially radioactive isotopes were employed, employed the natural radioactive isotope of lead, radium D, for the study of the course of lead in the organism.

The choice between the various types of isotope for a given investigation is at present mainly a matter of convenience. Stable and radioactive isotopes have their respective advantages and disadvantages. The analysis of the latter is generally more rapid and convenient, but the limited half-lifetime of some and the scarcity of others restrict their application to work that can be finished in a short time.[6]

Since the time Schoenheimer wrote the above, both stable and radioactive isotopes have become readily available; and experiments with labeled compounds are everyday events in modern laboratories. Generally the organism is unable to distinguish between a molecule of a compound bearing an isotopic atom from a normal, unlabeled molecule of the same substance. However, a definite isotope effect has been detected in biological experiments with heavy water (D_2O), which differs considerably in molecular weight from ordinary water (20:18). Mice or rats will die when about 35 per cent of their body fluids are replaced by deuterium oxide. Nevertheless, this is exceptional and has not prevented the widespread and successful use of very much smaller quantities of deuterium and also tritium (^3H) for tracer purposes. Some of the more useful isotopes for biological and biochemical studies are listed in Table 2–1.

■ BIOLOGICAL APPLICATIONS OF ISOTOPIC TRACERS

From the previous discussion it should be apparent that the use of radioactive and stable isotopic tracers presents a unique opportunity for studying living processes under physiological conditions. The method has been responsible not only for the concept of continuous turnover or dynamic state of tissue constituents but also for demonstration of the existence of a "metabolic pool" in living organisms. Food and the structural components of tissues continually are broken down to a *metabolic pool* of relatively simple substances which are then used for the resynthesis of tissue material and also other macromolecules. The key intermediates are generally small molecules containing just a few carbon atoms and include substances such as acetate, formate, and glycine.

As a result of the work of Konrad Bloch, G. Popjak, and J. W. Cornforth, it is now well established that all 27 carbon atoms of cholesterol are derived from acetate, 15 from the methyl carbon atoms and 12 from the carboxyl carbon. Their exact position in the complex steroid molecule also has been determined, and much of this infor-

TABLE 2–1

Some Isotopes of Importance in Tracer Studies

Isotope	Half life	Isotope	Half life
^2H (D)	∞	^{32}P	14 days
^3H (T)	12.5 years	^{35}S	87 days
^{13}C	∞	^{59}Fe	45 days
^{14}C	5560 years	^{131}I	8 days
^{18}O	∞		

mation was obtained by incubating rat liver slices with doubly labeled sodium acetate, $^{13}CH_3^{14}COONa$ and $^{14}CH_3^{13}COONa$ followed by isotopic analysis of the isolated cholesterol.

CH$_3$COOH ⟶

Acetic acid   Cholesterol

Another classic example of tracer research was carried out by J. M. Buchanan and his group who showed that the entire purine ring of uric acid, the major nitrogenous excretion product of birds, reptiles, and many invertebrates, could be formed by these animals from the simple substances ammonia, glycine, formate, and carbon dioxide. The actual incorporation, however, involves more complex intermediates.

Yet another outstanding example of the biological application of isotopes was the series of experiments conducted by David Shemin and David Rittenberg at Columbia University. They showed that the nitrogen in the heme component of hemoglobin was derived mainly from glycine; they then fed this amino acid labeled with the heavy isotope ^{15}N to human subjects. If red cells constantly are exchanging materials with their surroundings, a condition characteristic of practically all metabolic processes, the amount of labeled heme in blood should soon start to drop after an initial rise. It was found, however, that the concentration of labeled heme did not level off but continued to increase for nearly 25 days. It did not begin to drop until about the 100th day. It appears that hemoglobin in red blood cells is comparatively stable, and that heme is released only when the erythrocytes die and are broken down in the spleen. From these observations it was deduced that the average human red blood cell has a life span of about 130 days. These results have now been confirmed amply using hemoglobin labeled with radioactive iron (^{59}Fe).

Since small molecules such as glycine can give rise to a variety of products by several alternative metabolic pathways, it is virtually impossible to measure the rates of the biochemical reactions in the intact organism without using tracer techniques. As an example, some measure of the extent to which glucose is metabolized along two alternative pathways can be obtained with this sugar labeled either in the C-1 or the C-6 positions. During glycolysis both these carbon atoms are converted to the methyl group of pyruvate and metabolized in the same manner, whereas the C-1 and C-6 atoms of glucose are handled quite differently in the pentose phosphate pathway (Chap. 3).

In general, if a compound A is a specific precursor of compound B, the changes of the isotope concentration of the two compounds are related as shown in *Fig. 2–3*. Isotopes also have been used extensively to follow the anatomical distribution of administered isotopic material. Radioactive iodine (^{131}I) tends to become concentrated in the thyroid gland, and if a photographic film is applied to a cut section of this organ and then developed after exposure, localization of radioactivity can be demonstrated.

This technique of *autoradiography* recently has been extended to locate radioactively labeled substances not only in individual cells but also in the chromosomes and other structures within the cell. Tritium (^{3}H) is the isotope of choice for such studies; and experiments with ^{3}H-thymidine, which is used by cells almost exclusively for the synthesis of DNA, have provided a useful index for measur-

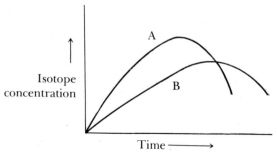

Isotope concentration

Time ⟶

Fig. 2–3. Relationship between isotope concentration of compound A and its metabolic product B.

ing rates of cell division. The percentage of cells bearing the label indicates what proportion of the cells is synthesizing DNA at a given time. One interesting fact that has emerged from such studies is the discovery that in actively proliferating tissues, such as the intestinal mucosa, the two daughter cells of a cell division usually have different destinies, and only one of each pair divides again. On the other hand, during malignant growth almost every daughter cell is capable of further division (see also Vol. IV).

Finally, isotopes have proven of value in immunological investigation, in accurate measurements of the circulating blood volume, and in numerous other biological problems of nutrition, photosynthesis, and membrane permeability, to mention but a few examples. It is small wonder that the tracer technique has changed our whole concept of living processes, and that the steady state condition of tissue constituents was hardly suspected before the introduction of isotopes. Once again in the words of Schoenheimer:

> It can readily be understood why the classical methods of metabolism, which were mainly limited to the measurement of changes in amount or relative composition, failed to detect this dynamic state.[7]

1. William S. Beck, *Modern Science and the Nature of Life,* by permission of Harcourt, Brace & World, Inc., New York, and Macmillan & Company, Ltd., London, 1957, pp. 203–204.
2. Reprinted by permission of the publishers from Rudolph Schoenheimer, *The Dynamic State of Body Constituents,* Cambridge, Mass.: Harvard University Press, Copyright, 1942, by the President and Fellows of Harvard College, pp. 64–65.
3. H. A. Krebs, "Cyclic Processes in Living Matter," *Enzymologia,* 12 (1946), 97–100.
4. A. L. Lehninger, *Biogenetics: The Molecular Basis of Energy Transformations* (New York: W. A. Benjamin, Inc., 1965), pp. 56–57.
5. D. E. Green and S. Fleischer, "On the Molecular Organization of Biological Transducing Systems," in *Horizons in Biochemistry,* ed. M. Kasha and B. Pullman (New York: Academic Press, Inc., 1962), pp. 381–382.
6. Schoenheimer, *op. cit.,* pp. 5–7.
7. *Ibid.,* p. 24.

CHAPTER 3 Energy-Yielding
Multienzyme Systems

■ LIFE UNDER AEROBIC AND ANAEROBIC CONDITIONS

Solar energy is the ultimate source of all biological energy. Green plants containing chlorophyll can manufacture organic nutrients from inorganic compounds, binding the energy of sunlight during photosynthesis and storing it as potential chemical energy. These self-supporting, *autotrophic* organisms, which also include many bacteria, can derive all their cellular carbon from carbon dioxide; but *heterotrophic* organisms depend upon more complex organic molecules for their source of energy.

The breakdown of energy-yielding carbohydrate that occurs during the metabolic reactions of the cell can be carried out either in the absence of oxygen (anaerobically) by *fermentation* or *glycolysis,* or in the presence of oxygen (aerobically) by *respiration.* The fact that organisms are able to draw nourishment and energy from glucose in the absence of oxygen was realized over a century ago by Pasteur who described fermentation as "La vie sans air [life without oxygen]." He also recognized that living cells which require oxygen for normal growth and function also possess the capacity to derive energy from glucose by degrading it under anaerobic conditions.

From the energy metabolism viewpoint, the most important single factor in the environment is the presence or absence of oxygen. Without this element, which is a very effective electron acceptor, only a small part of the energy of organic compounds can be released; and this low energy yield places a limit on the kind of life activities that organisms can develop through evolution. Nevertheless, yeast and most microorganisms thrive in the total absence of oxygen; and, in fact, some anaerobes, such as *Bacillus botulinus,* cannot tolerate oxygen and die if exposed to it. They are called *obligate anaerobes,* as opposed to organisms like yeast which still grow and multiply in the presence of oxygen and are called *facultative anaerobes.*

Animals generally are considered to be aerobes, and certainly all the higher forms are dependent upon oxygen for survival. However, animals are usually able to work beyond the capacity of the body to supply oxygen needed for immediate purposes and thus develop an *oxygen debt.* They liberate the energy required for the work in progress by anaerobic reactions and then subsequently, during the recovery period, use extra oxygen to repay the debt by reoxidizing the reduced metabolites (such as lactic acid) that have accumulated. This means that most animals can survive for a time under relatively anaerobic conditions. Plants, like animals, are essentially aerobes; but many are capable of tolerating considerable periods of anaerobiosis.

It must be stressed that although oxygen is the ultimate oxidizing agent under aerobic conditions, many oxidative reactions can occur without the participation of this element; in fact, most biological oxidations occur by enzyme-catalyzed removal of hydrogen (dehydrogenation) or by loss of electrons (e.g., $Fe^{++} \rightarrow Fe^{+++} + e^-$). However, since neither electrons nor hydrogen atoms can accumulate as such within living organisms, every oxidation must be accompanied by a corresponding reduction:

$$AH_2 + B \rightarrow BH_2 + A$$

In this coupled oxido-reduction, AH_2 is the *reductant* (hydrogen donor), and B is the *oxidant* (hydrogen acceptor), with often a coenzyme such as NAD or NADP (see Vol. I) acting as intermediate carrier between the two substrates AH_2 and B:

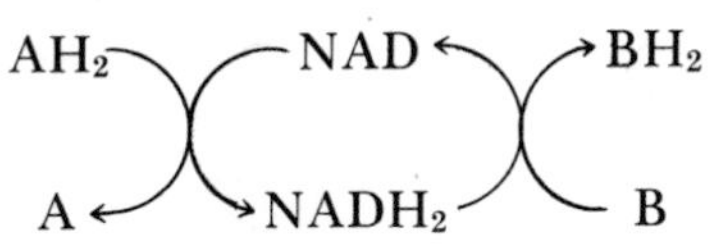

The tendency for any particular atom, ion, or molecule to lose or gain an electron is measured by its oxidation-reduction (redox) potential which is thus indicative of oxidizing or reducing intensity. Substances with a high redox potential are able to oxidize those with a lower value and become reduced themselves in the process. However, even though a reaction is thermodynamically feasible, it may not occur necessarily at a detectable rate, unless the appropriate enzymes are present. $NADH_2$, by itself, is quite stable in the presence of oxygen, even though this reduced coenzyme has a very low redox potential.

■ **FERMENTATION AND GLYCOLYSIS**

Carbohydrates are a major source of energy for living organisms. Generally they are stored in the form of polymers of glucose, such as starch or glycogen, and are accumulated within the cells in times of abundant supply to be used later when there is a demand for energy production.

The intermediary metabolism of glucose may be divided into an anaerobic phase and an aerobic one during which aerobic organisms oxidize the products formed under anaerobic conditions. In the absence of oxygen, glucose is converted by the enzymes of yeast and many microorganisms to ethyl alcohol and carbon dioxide; under similar conditions, muscle and other animal tissues, as well as certain bacteria (lactobacilli), convert glucose to lactic acid. The former process is known as *fermentation* and the latter as *glycolysis,* but they are very similar and proceed as far as pyruvic acid by a common pathway.

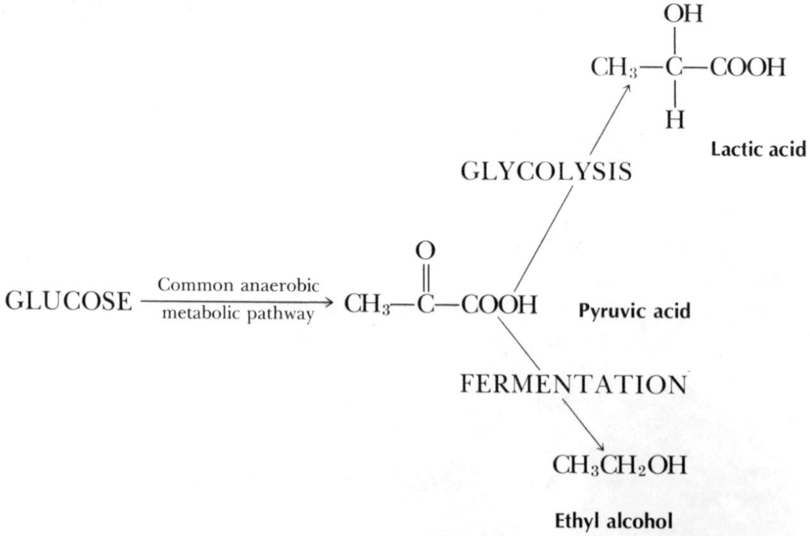

$$
\begin{array}{c}
\overset{\displaystyle OH}{\underset{\displaystyle H}{CH_3-\!\!\overset{|}{\underset{|}{C}}\!\!-COOH}} \\
\text{\textbf{Lactic acid}}
\end{array}
$$

GLYCOLYSIS

$$
GLUCOSE \xrightarrow[\text{metabolic pathway}]{\text{Common anaerobic}} CH_3-\overset{\displaystyle O}{\overset{\|}{C}}-COOH \quad \text{\textbf{Pyruvic acid}}
$$

FERMENTATION

$$CH_3CH_2OH$$

Ethyl alcohol

The sequence of reactions as it exists today in fermentation and glycolysis was established by the pioneers of biochemistry. Systematic study of the enzymes responsible for the catalysis of these metabolic processes began only after 1897. That year Hans and Eduard Büchner succeeded in obtaining from yeast a cell-free extract which was able to convert glucose to ethyl alcohol. In the words of E. Baldwin:

> Like many other great discoveries, that of the Büchners had in it an element of chance. They were primarily interested in making cell-free

extracts of yeast for therapeutic purposes, and this they accomplished by grinding yeast with sand, mixing it with kieselguhr, and squeezing out the juice with a hydraulic press. There then arose the problem of preserving their products. Since it was to be used for experiments on animals, the ordinary antiseptics could not be used as preservatives, so they tried the method usual in kitchen-chemistry of adding large amounts of sucrose. This led to the momentous discovery that sucrose is rapidly fermented by yeast juice. Here for the first time, fermentation was observed in the complete absence of living cells, and at last it was possible to study the processes of alcoholic fermentation independently of all the other processes—growth, multiplication and excretion—which accompany fermentation in the living yeast cell.[1]

Later, after Otto Meyerhof had found that extracts of mammalian muscle cause the anaerobic degradation of glycogen to lactic acid, the study of fermentation and glycolysis developed in parallel, and results obtained with one system helped to elucidate problems that arose during studies of the other. Phosphorylated sugars were shown to be formed during both fermentation and glycolysis, and many enzymes and coenzymes were found to be involved in the complex sequence of reactions leading to the formation of ethyl alcohol or lactic acid from glucose. In both processes pyruvic acid is produced first, but organisms which lack the enzyme, carboxylase, are unable to convert pyruvic acid to acetaldehyde and, under anaerobic conditions, regenerate NAD by reducing pyruvate (*Fig. 3–1*). The whole series of events is known as the *Embden-Meyerhof pathway* in honor of the investigators who were the main architects of this scheme; however, many others including J. Parnas, Sir Arthur Harden, W. Young, R. Robinson, the Coris, and Otto Warburg also made significant contributions.

The overall reaction may be summarized as follows:

$$C_6H_{12}O_6 \xrightarrow[\text{Glycolysis}]{\text{Fermentation}} \begin{array}{l} 2C_2H_5OH + 2CO_2 \\ 2CH_3CH(OH)COOH \end{array}$$

$$2NAD \longrightarrow 2NADH_2 \longrightarrow 2NAD, \text{ no net change}$$

$$\left.\begin{array}{l} 2ATP \longrightarrow 2ADP \\ 4ADP \longrightarrow 4ATP \end{array}\right\} \text{ net gain of two molecules of ATP}$$

Therefore, in both fermentation and glycolysis ATP provides the "spark" to start the sequence of events that leads to the generation of more ATP (two molecules per molecule of glucose broken down). This is the main function of both these fundamental biochemical processes; and, if glucose were broken down directly, much of the

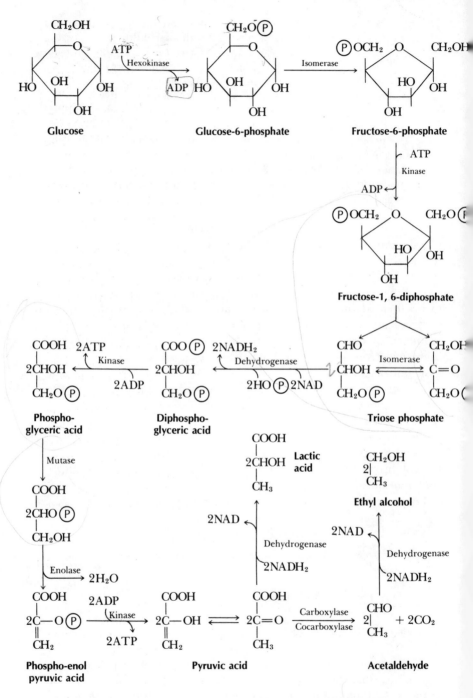

Fig. 3–1. The breakdown of glucose to ethyl alcohol (fermentation) or to lactic acid (glycolysis). Both processes have a common pathway to pyruvic acid (Embden-Meyerhof pathway).

intrinsic energy of the sugar would be liberated as heat and lost to the organism instead of being stored as ATP. It is well known from experimental data that thermodynamic efficiency is greatest when the number of steps in the reaction is large and approaches complete reversibility. By means of a stepwise degradation, much of the energy released is trapped in ATP and transferred to wherever it is needed.

The enzymes responsible for fermentation and glycolysis are present in the soluble matrix of the cell; and, unlike the respiratory enzymes which are localized in the mitochondria, they are not associated with any particular organelle. Although glucose itself is easily capable of crossing cell membranes, its phosphorylated derivatives are unable to diffuse out of the cell; and the hexokinase reaction by which glucose is converted to glucose-6-phosphate, therefore, provides a mechanism for the "capture" of glucose.

Generally, however, energy requirements of the organism are not provided by glucose itself but by stored carbohydrate macromolecules such as glycogen of liver and muscle or the starch of plants. These depot polysaccharides are mobilized by phosphorylytic cleavage to glucose-1-phosphate (*Fig. 3–2*) instead of by hydrolysis to monosaccharide molecules (glucose) as during digestion.

Glucose-1-phosphate is converted readily to glucose-6-phosphate by a specific phosphoglucomutase. Although the phosphorylase reaction is readily reversible, the role of the enzyme is largely degradative in nature. A different reaction involving uridine diphosphate glucose is involved in the synthesis of polysaccharides from sugar phosphates (Chap. 4).

The reversal of glycolysis also involves several enzymes that are not operative in the forward sequence. One of the major principles governing metabolism is that if a compound gives rise to a product by way of certain intermediates, it will be resynthesized by a pathway that is either partly or completely independent of the forward reaction.

■ ALTERNATIVE PATHWAYS OF CARBOHYDRATE METABOLISM

Although the Embden-Meyerhof scheme is the principal pathway for the initial breakdown of glucose in most biological systems, it is by no means the only metabolic route for this process. The existence of alternative pathways was indicated first by the fact that in some tissues the classical inhibitors of fermentation and glycolysis, such as iodoacetate and fluoride, had little effect on the utilization of glucose; these results were later confirmed by tracer studies.

Of some importance is the alternative route of carbohydrate metabolism which involves the degradation of glucose-6-phosphate by way of pentose phosphates and is consequently known as the *pentose phosphate pathway.* It has also been called the *hexose monophos-phate shunt*, since it involves reactions that bypass those of the Emb-den-Meyerhof pathway.

The pentose phosphate pathway occurs in both animal and plant tissues. Knowledge of this pathway has emerged from the initial studies of Otto Warburg, Frank Dickens, and Fritz Lipmann which were later followed by those of B. L. Horecker and Efraim Racker. The special advantages that accrue to the organism by utilization of this pathway, other than pentose formation for the synthesis of nu-cleotides (Chap. 4), is that it produces most of the NADPH$_2$ required

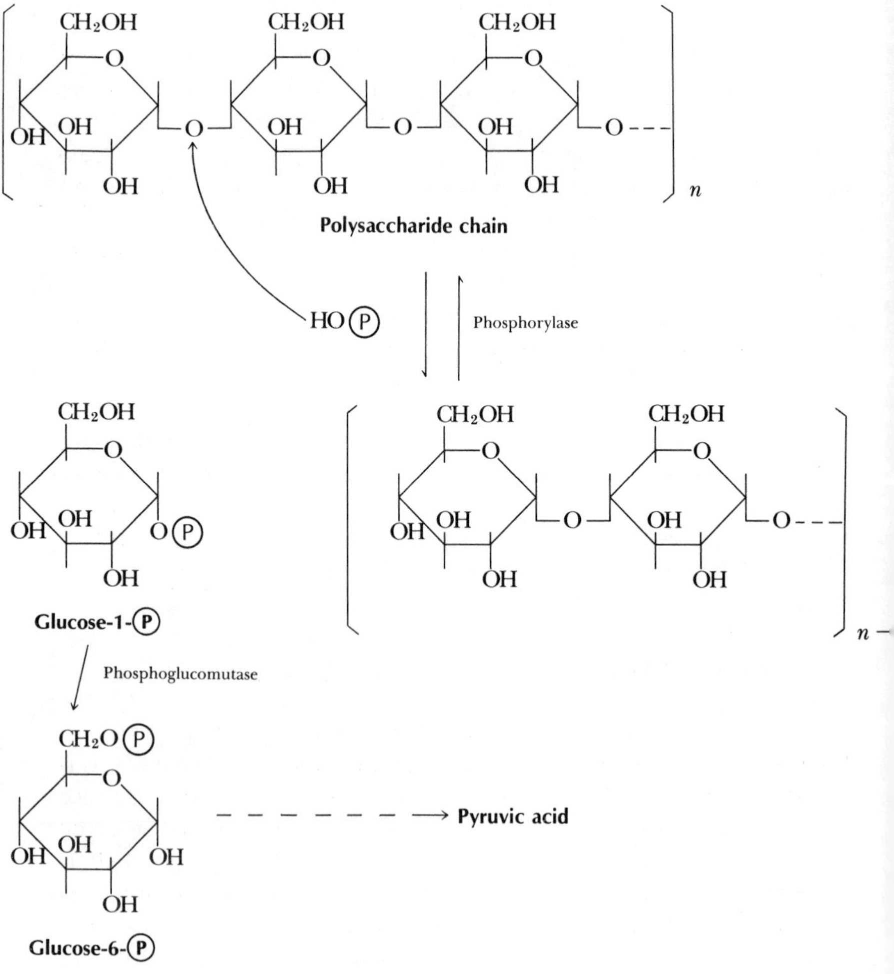

Fig. 3-2. The breakdown of polysaccharides to pyruvic acid. The initial reaction in-volves phosphorylytic cleavage to glucose-1-phosphate.

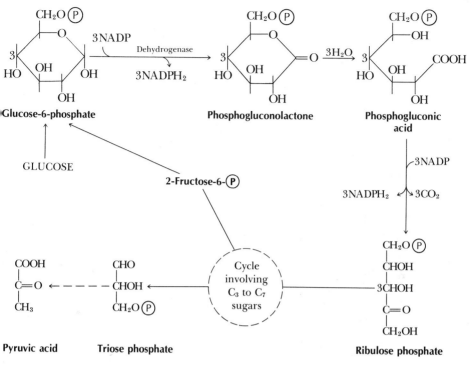

Fig. 3–3. The pentose phosphate pathway ($3C_6 \rightarrow 2C_6 + C_3 + 3CO_2$).

for synthetic reactions within the cell. In addition, the pentose phosphate pathway provides a means of degrading glucose to carbon dioxide without participation of the citric acid cycle (see below), and it is also involved intimately in the interconversion of carbon compounds produced in the initial stages of photosynthesis. Furthermore, no additional ATP is required to break down the sugar by this alternative route, once glucose-6-phosphate has been formed.

Efforts employing animal tissues to determine the significance of the pentose phosphate pathway in the metabolism of glucose have indicated that this pathway may be more important than glycolysis in the mammary gland, adipose tissue, testis, and adrenal cortex. These tissues are concerned with the synthesis of fatty acids or steroids and, therefore, require $NADPH_2$. On the other hand, glucose or glycogen are broken down in muscle almost exclusively by glycolysis. There is also evidence that the pentose phosphate pathway may be the more significant one in some plant tissues, especially leaves, and that it may assume greater importance as the cells mature.

The cell, therefore, seems to have evolved multiple pathways which ensure that certain key intermediates ($NADPH_2$, pentose phosphates) are formed under all circumstances. Yet other routes of glucose breakdown have been identified in microorganisms. In one of these known as the *Entner-Doudoroff pathway*, 6-phosphogluconic acid is converted to a hexose phosphate intermediate which is then cleaved to form pyruvate and glyceraldehyde-3-phosphate.

■ THE CITRIC ACID CYCLE

The various anaerobic pathways of glucose degradation described so far provide only a very inefficient mechanism for the synthesis of ATP, and a great deal of energy is still available in the final product. In fact, only about 7 per cent of the available energy of glucose is released when lactate is formed during glycolysis.

It soon became apparent to the early investigators such as Szent Györgyi and T. Thunberg that pyruvate and lactate were being oxidized further to carbon dioxide and water, but it remained for H. A. Krebs and W. A. Johnson to propose that it occurred by way of a metabolic cycle involving citric acid as an intermediate. It has been variously termed the "citric acid cycle," the "Krebs cycle," and the "tricarboxylic acid cycle." (*Fig. 3–4*) According to Krebs and Johnson:

> If it is true that the oxidation of citric acid is a stage in the catalytic action of citric acid then it follows that citric acid must be regenerated eventually from one of the products of oxidation. We are thus led to examine whether citric acid can be resynthesized from any of the intermediates of the citric acid breakdown. Systematic experiments show that indeed large quantities of citric acid are formed if oxaloacetic acid is added to muscle anaerobically, whilst all the other intermediates yield no citric acid under the same conditions. It is because the synthesis of citric acid from oxaloacetic acid does not require molecular oxygen and because citric acid is stable in the tissue anaerobically that it is possible to demonstrate the synthesis of citric acid in a simple experiment.
>
> Minced pigeon breast muscle was suspended as usual in 3 volumes phosphate buffer and 3 ml suspension were measured into a conical manometric flask the sidearm of which contained 0.3 ml 1 M oxaloacetate. In the centre chamber a stick of yellow phosphorus was placed and the gas space was filled with nitrogen. After the removal of oxygen the oxaloacetate was added to the tissue and the flask was shaken in the water bath for 20 mins. During this period about 1000 μl CO_2 were evolved. After the incubation, the suspension was quantitatively transferred into 25 ml 6% trichloracetic acid and the volume was made up to 50 ml. Citric acid was determined in the filtrate and 0.0131 millimoles citric acid were found. No citrate was present in the controls.
>
> The experiment shows that muscle is capable of forming large quantities of citric acid if oxaloacetic acid is present. . . .[2]

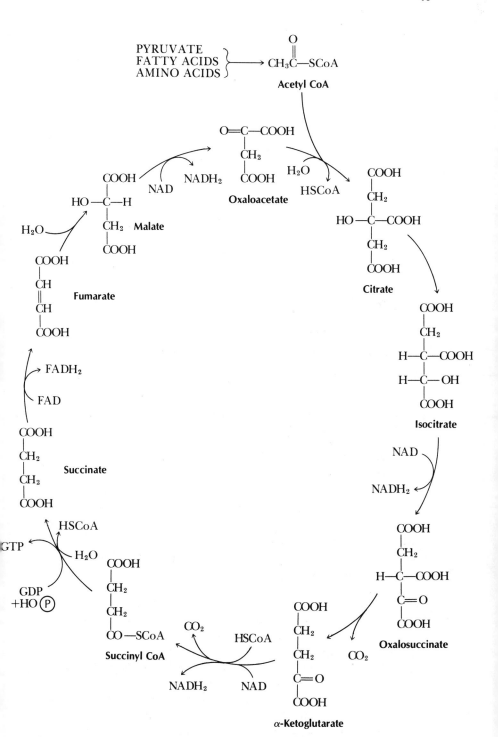

Fig. 3-4. The citric acid (Krebs) cycle.

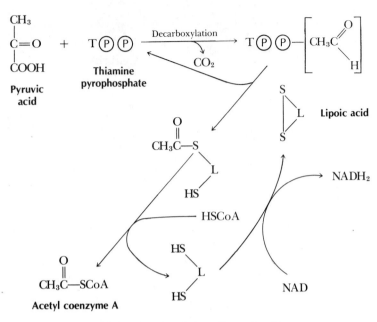

Fig. 3–5. Oxidative decarboxylation of pyruvic acid.

They end their classic scientific paper by stating that:

> . . . the quantitative data suggest that the "citric acid cycle" is the pref-
> erential pathway through which carbohydrate is oxidised in animal
> tissues.[2]

Pyruvic acid itself is not an intermediate in the citric acid cycle.
It is converted first to acetyl coenzyme A by a complex series of
oxidative reactions involving thiamine (vitamin B_1) pyrophosphate,
lipoic acid, coenzyme A, NAD, and an enzyme complex known as
pyruvic oxidase. This process of oxidative decarboxylation is shown
in *Fig. 3–5.*

Acetyl coenzyme A, which is also known as *active acetate* because it
behaves as if it were a highly reactive form of acetic acid, is also
formed by oxidative degradation of fatty acids (discussed later) and
is a key metabolite in many biosynthetic reactions.

Pyruvate can react also with CO_2 to yield oxaloacetate, and the
Krebs cycle is initiated by the condensation of oxaloacetate with
acetyl coenzyme A to form a six-carbon compound containing three
carboxyl groups—namely citrate. This last compound, after initial
isomerization to isocitrate as shown in the scheme, then undergoes
a series of decarboxylation and oxidation reactions, with the eventual

formation of oxaloacetate which closes the cycle. One molecule of acetyl coenzyme A, therefore, is oxidized at each turn of the cycle, and pyruvic acid formed during glycolysis is completely degraded to CO_2 and H_2O.

$$2CH_3COCOOH + 5O_2 \rightarrow 6\ CO_2 + 4H_2O + \text{Energy}$$

There are five oxidative steps, and in each of these reactions two electrons are removed from the substrate and pass along the respiratory chain (see below) to react eventually with oxygen. It is during electron transfer along the respiratory chain that ATP is generated. As mentioned earlier, the citric acid cycle enzymes are located in the mitochondria in close association with the enzymes concerned with electron transport and oxidative phosphorylation (see below).

The Krebs cycle is widely distributed in nature and occurs in all respiring tissues of animals ranging from protozoa to mammals. It occurs also in higher plants and in many aerobic microorganisms, although in some lower forms of life it may be functioning only in part. In addition, many plants and microorganisms contain an enzyme, *isocitritase*, which catalyzes the splitting of isocitrate to glyoxylate and succinate and provides an alternative route (the glyoxylate bypass) for the citric acid cycle. The glyoxylate that is formed condenses with acetate in the presence of *malic synthetase* to form malate, the latter then is oxidized to oxaloacetate (*Fig. 3–6*).

The acetyl coenzyme A that enters the cycle is derived mainly from fatty acids by β-oxidation (discussed later), and the oxaloacetate formed may be converted to phosphoenol pyruvate and then to carbohydrate by the reversal of glycolysis. This process involves another high-energy phosphate compound, inosine triphosphate (ITP):

COOH ITP
|
C=O   Enzyme
| IDP CO_2
CH_2
|
COOH

Oxaloacetate

COOH
|
C—O(P) ⟶ (Reversal of glycolysis) ⟶ **CARBOHYDRATE**
‖
CH_2

Phosphoenol pyruvate

This role of converting fat to carbohydrate is supported by the fact that glyoxylate cycle enzymes are present in high concentration in germinating seeds having a high oil content but are absent from seeds depending on starch rather than fat as a source of energy.

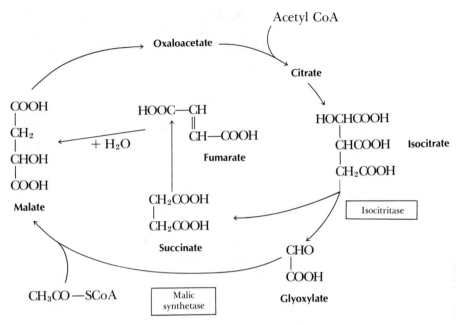

Fig. 3–6. The glyoxylate cycle.

Both isocitritase and malic synthetase are inducible enzymes (Chap. 5) which disappear when the seed's fat deposits have been depleted.

Although both the Krebs and glyoxylate cycles are considered most often in terms of the further oxidation of pyruvate or acetyl coenzyme A for the generation of energy, they are useful in the production and utilization of the carbon skeletons of many compounds including amino acids (discussed later).

■ ELECTRON TRANSPORT AND OXIDATIVE PHOSPHORYLATION

The common metabolic pathway for channeling of electrons to oxygen is termed the *electron transport system* or the *respiratory chain,* and most of the ATP used by organisms is formed as a result of the operation of this sequence of reactions. The respiratory chain is the "power train" of the mitochondrion, the site of conversion of respiratory energy into high energy phosphates, mechanochemical energy, and osmotic energy.

Details of the respiratory chain have proved difficult to study, because the enzymes of this system occur in the mitochondria as multienzyme aggregates within the electron transfer particles (Chap. 1). However, it appears that the major components of the respiratory chain are NAD-linked dehydrogenases, flavoproteins, coenzyme Q, and the cytochromes arranged in a chain of increasing redox potential (see below). The electrons flow from the substrate via the pyridine and flavin nucleotides to the cytochromes and finally to oxygen (*Fig. 3–7*).

This scheme applies to substrates which are oxidized by dehydrogenases requiring NAD as coenzyme, but certain biological oxidations utilize a flavin rather than a pyridine nucleotide as hydrogen acceptor. Thus NAD is bypassed when succinate is oxidized to fumarate by succinic dehydrogenase in the citric acid cycle, and the electrons flow directly to flavoprotein.

A group of quinones, the ubiquinones or coenzyme Q have been implicated in electron transport, but there is still considerable uncertainty about their role. They are found not only in mitochondria but also in cell nuclei and microsomes; they appear to be associated with membranes. In addition, Chance has shown that endogenous coenzyme Q of the mitochondria is not oxidized and reduced at rates compatible with the rates of known electron carriers.

The citric acid cycle and the respiratory chain are, however, only the preparatory phase for a very important process first proposed by H. M. Kalckar and V. A. Belitser in 1937 — *oxidative phosphorylation*. The details of the reaction still are not understood well, but essentially ATP is generated from ADP and inorganic phosphate at the expense of energy derived from the oxidation of the Krebs cycle intermediates by the enzymes of the respiratory chain. Several active intermediates have been invoked, including a form of NAD-phos-

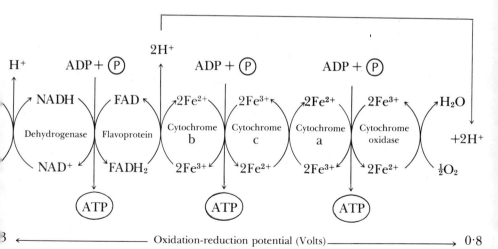

Fig. 3–7. The respiratory chain (coenzyme Q has been omitted from this scheme).

phate which in the presence of mitochondrial particles can transfer its phosphate groups to ADP.

Normally, oxidative phosphorylation is linked to electron transport in intact mitochondria; and if phosphorylation cannot occur because of a lack of ADP or inorganic phosphate, the oxidation of intermediates of the Krebs cycle will be inhibited. However, a number of substances such as 2,4-dinitrophenol, or the hormone, thyroxine, are able to dissociate the flow of electrons from the phosphorylation of ADP. They "uncouple" oxidation from phosphorylation, and under these circumstances the free energy of the respiratory process is lost to the cell and dissipated as heat. It has also been possible to separate the electron transfer chain in a reversible manner from the components of the phosphorylating system; when these particles were combined with a nonphosphorylating soluble fraction from mitochondria, the mixture catalyzed oxidative phosphorylation.

ATP is believed to be generated at the sites indicated in *Fig. 3–7*. This type of process is known also as "respiratory chain phosphorylation," to distinguish it from "substrate level phosphorylation" illustrated by the formation of ATP from diphosphoglycerate or phosphoenol pyruvate during fermentation or glycolysis.

It is apparent from *Fig. 3–7* (based on experimental results) that the oxidation of each molecule of $NADH_2$ by O_2 results in the formation of three molecules of ATP, whereas only two ATP molecules are produced from a reaction in which flavoprotein is the direct hydrogen acceptor. Using this line of approach it has been possible (1) to show (table 3–1) that the total oxidation of pyruvate leads to a net synthesis of 15 molecules of ATP and also (2) to estimate the number of high-energy phosphate molecules synthesized when glucose is degraded to CO_2 and H_2O aerobically.

The conversion of one molecule of glucose to two molecules of pyruvate results in the formation of two molecules of ATP by substrate level phosphorylation; the further oxidation of this pyruvate in the citric acid cycle yields another 2×15, i.e., 30 high-energy phosphate molecules. In addition, when glucose is broken down under aerobic conditions, the two $NADH_2$ molecules that are formed are oxidized by the respiratory chain enzymes instead of being utilized to reduce pyruvate to lactate; and a further four* molecules of ATP are generated. Thus a total of 36 high-energy phosphate molecules are produced for each molecule of glucose broken down aerobically, a yield that is almost 20 times higher than that obtained under anaerobic conditions.

---

* Extramitochondrial $NADH_2$ is oxidized by a "shuttle system" and generates only two molecules of ATP.

TABLE 3–1

Phosphorylation of ADP During Oxidation
of Pyruvate Via Citric Acid Cycle

Reaction	Carrier	Molecules of ATP Formed
Pyruvate $\longrightarrow$ Acetyl CoA	Lipoic acid $\longrightarrow$ NAD	3
Isocitrate $\longrightarrow$ α-Ketoglutarate	NADP $\longrightarrow$ NAD	3
α-Ketoglutarate $\longrightarrow$ Succinyl CoA	Lipoic acid $\longrightarrow$ NAD	3
GDP GTP*		
Succinyl CoA $\longrightarrow$ Succinate		1
Succinate $\longrightarrow$ Fumarate	FAD	2
Malate $\longrightarrow$ Oxaloacetate	NAD	3
		15 (Total)

* Equivalent to ATP in energy content.

In the light of these findings, it is interesting that Pasteur recognized many years ago that glycolysis is slower under aerobic than under anaerobic conditions. This inhibition of glycolysis by oxygen, known as the *Pasteur effect,* results in the conservation of nutrient glucose when the energy yield per molecule of glucose is increased.

The mechanism by which ATP formation is coupled to the flow of electrons along the respiratory chain is under intensive study, and many groups are looking for active intermediates. However, in the words of Lehninger:

> Some workers feel that the mechanism of oxidative phosphorylation may not ultimately be resolved in terms of the classical experimental approach to analysis of multienzyme systems; that is, the isolation and purification of the separate enzymes, the reconstruction of the over-all system and finally the analysis of the structure and action of the active sites of the enzymes involved. Perhaps the mitochondrial membrane per se is an integral part of the system, required not simply as a piece of "floor space" but as a necessary element in the transformation of respiratory energy into osmotic and mechanical energy as well, as postulated by Lehninger. In fact, Mitchell has gone so far as to suggest that oxidative phosphorylation is the consequence of vectorial transport mechanisms across the mitochondrial membrane rather than the result of the action of a scalar multienzyme system having no structural or directional polarization.[3]

■ FATTY ACID OXIDATION

The lipids not only are vital structural constituents of cell membranes and of subcellular organelles but also are stored in large amounts as triglycerides (fat), particularly in animals where they provide a concentrated supply of readily available energy. Fat, in fact, yields over twice as many calories per gram as either carbohydrate or protein, and most of this is liberated during the aerobic breakdown of its component fatty acids.

The oxidation of fatty acids, which occurs in the mitochondria, proceeds by several distinct steps; but the final product is acetyl coenzyme A which is oxidized in the citric acid cycle as if it had arisen from pyruvate.

Fatty acids themselves are relatively inert chemically and are broken down in the cell only when they become converted to high-energy

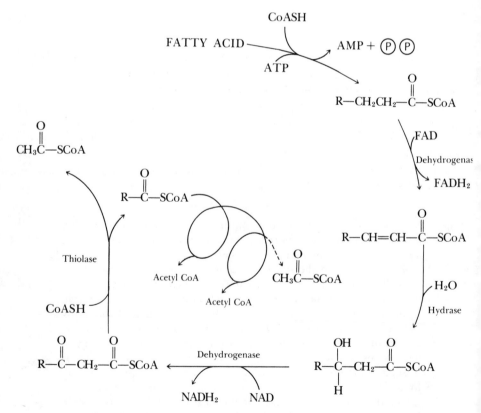

Fig. 3–8. The β-oxidative breakdown of fatty acids to acetyl coenzyme A.

Table 3–2
*Phosphorylation of ADP During Complete Oxidation
of Palmitate Via Citric Acid Cycle*

Reaction	Molecules of ATP Formed
Palmitate → Palmitoyl-CoA	−1
Palmitoyl-CoA → 8 Acetyl-CoA	
7 FADH$_2$ → 7 FAD	14 (7 × 2)
7 NADH$_2$ → 7 NAD	21 (7 × 3)
8 Acetyl-CoA → 16 CO$_2$ + 8H$_2$O + 8CoA	96 (8 × 12)
	130 (Total)

thioesters. This activation requires energy in the form of ATP and also the participation of coenzyme A and the enzyme thiokinase.

$$R-CH_2CH_2\overset{O}{\overset{\|}{C}}-OH + ATP + CoA-SH \xrightarrow[Mg^{++}]{Thiokinase}$$

$$R-CH_2CH_2\overset{O}{\overset{\|}{C}}-SCoA + AMP + \textcircled{P}\,\textcircled{P}$$

The CoA derivatives of the fatty acids are then oxidized by a series of reactions referred to as *β-oxidation*, since they involve the formation of a β-keto acid intermediate (*Fig. 3–8*).

The end product of β-oxidation is acetyl CoA, and this oxidative system is found not only in animal but also in bacterial and plant tissues. Each molecule of a common fatty acid such as palmitate (C$_{15}$H$_{31}$COOH) will give rise to eight molecules of acetyl CoA by seven* full turns in this helical scheme; and, since each molecule of acetyl CoA can then be further oxidized by the citric acid cycle, a total of 130 molecules of ATP will be generated overall (Table 3–2). Clearly, fatty acids and, therefore, fats also are a very effective source of energy.

■ NITROGEN METABOLISM

Amino acids, in common with other compounds of low molecular weight, are not stored by cells; and, with the exception of seeds, there is no evidence for the existence of storage proteins which can yield amino acids for metabolic purposes. Amino acids present in excess of the immediate needs are used as a general source of carbon atoms,

*Two molecules of acetyl CoA are produced at the final turn of the helix.

and energy is released by reactions which destroy the amino acid molecule.

The first step in degradation of amino acids involves removal of the amino group by a process of *deamination;* this may be either oxidative or nonoxidative. The amino acid group can also be removed by *transamination*, but in this case it is transferred to the carbon skeleton of another amino acid. These different types of reactions are illustrated below:

Deamination

(1)

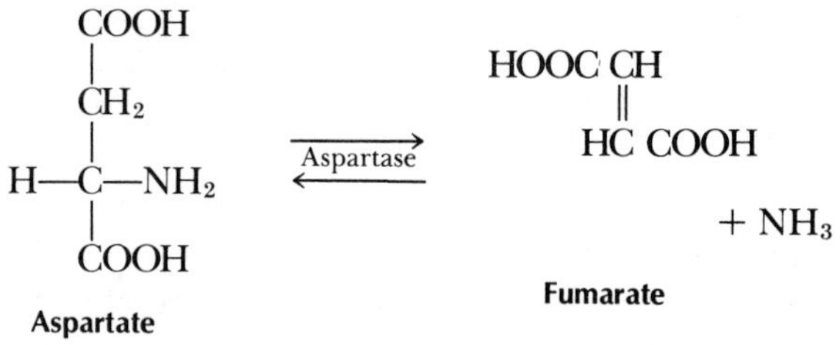

Aspartate → (Aspartase) ⇌ Fumarate + NH_3

Oxidative deamination

(2)

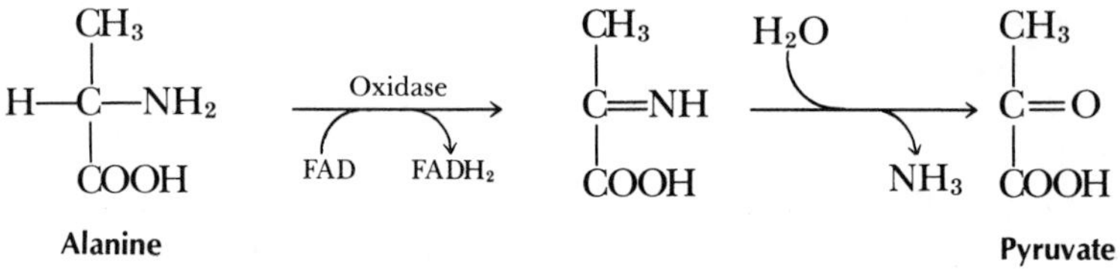

Alanine → (Oxidase, FAD → FADH$_2$) → (H_2O) → Pyruvate + NH_3

(3)

Glutamate + NAD^+ + H_2O ⇌ (Dehydrogenase) α-Ketoglutarate + $NADH$ + NH_4^+

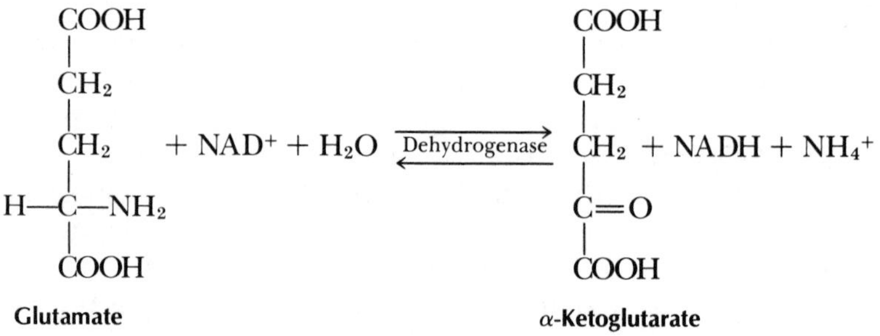

Transamination

(4)

Aspartate + α-Ketoglutarate ⇌ (Transaminase + Pyridoxal phosphate) Oxaloacetate + Glutamate

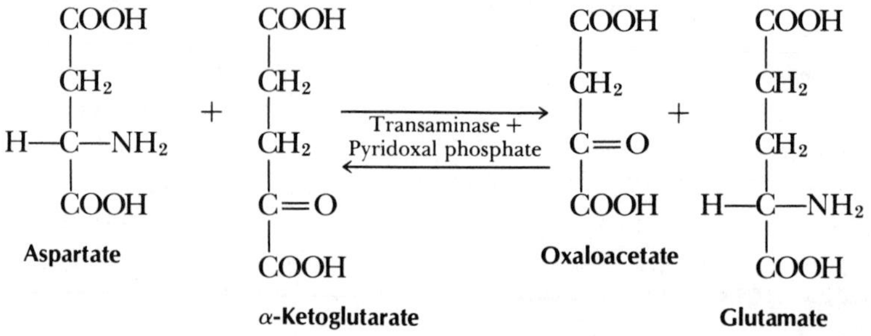

Reactions (1) and (2) occur mainly in bacteria and fungi, but (3) and (4) are universal biochemical reactions and yield α-keto acids. Compounds such as pyruvate, oxaloacetate, and α-ketoglutarate which are intermediates of glucose oxidation can then be oxidized further in the citric acid cycle; while others are converted to such metabolites by more indirect pathways. Thus the carbon chains of amino acids can, in general, be oxidized by the normal processes of carbohydrate metabolism with the production of ATP, or they even can be used for the production of storage polysaccharides by the reversal of glycolysis.

Although not involved in energy formation, it seems appropriate at this stage to inquire about the fate of the ammonia produced during deamination of amino acids. Ammonia is very toxic, and its accumulation in appreciable concentrations either in cells or in extra-cellular fluids is incompatible with life. Organisms which live in aqueous environments can dispose easily of this ammonia, since it is readily diffusible and can escape into the surrounding water; but organisms which live on land are unable to do this and have de-veloped mechanisms for converting ammonia either into urea or uric acid.

According to Joseph Needham, the choice between urea and uric acid formation is determined by the conditions under which the embryo develops. Thus the mammalian embryo, which grows in close contact with the circulatory system of the mother and has at its disposal the entire water resources and excretory apparatus of the maternal organism excretes urea; whereas the embryos of birds and reptiles, which develop in a hard-shelled egg in an external environment, excrete uric acid. The eggs are laid with just enough water to see them through the hatching period, and the production of urea in such a closed system would, in the words of Needham, "be sufficient to give the embryo a bad headache at the very least. In which case natural selection would hardly have preserved it for our entertainment."[4] Uric acid is produced, therefore, by these embryos, and this substance which, unlike urea, is very insoluble precipitates out in the allantoic sac on the interior surface of the shell. These characteristics essential for the development of the em-bryo are carried over to the adult organism.

The formation of uric acid follows closely the mechanism for the biosynthesis of the purine component of nucleic acids (Chap. 4); whereas urea is formed by a cycle of reactions (*Fig. 3–9*) first proposed by Krebs in 1932. It has been called the "urea cycle" and also the "ornithine cycle."

From the energy viewpoint, the formation of urea is wasteful, since it is accomplished by the utilization of three molecules of ATP; but this is the price paid by the organism to escape the deleterious effects of high concentrations of ammonia.

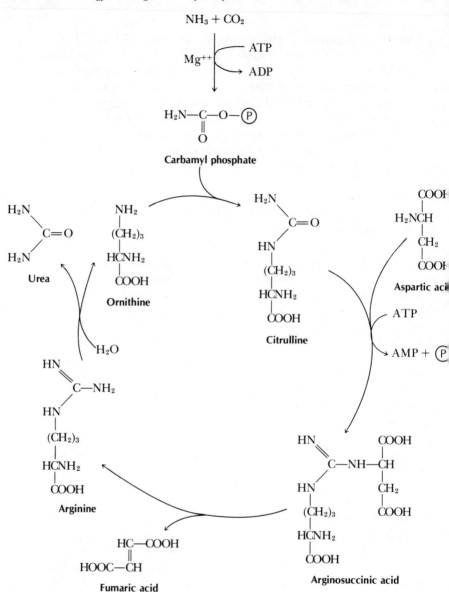

Fig. 3-9. The urea cycle.

Although large amounts of ammonia are toxic to the organism, it is nevertheless one of the most important, single intermediates in nitrogen metabolism. Thus most organisms when supplied with an adequate source of utilizable carbon compounds can use ammonia readily as the principal metabolic source of amino acids and proteins. Many microorganisms can grow, that is, synthesize protein, in a culture medium containing ammonium salts as the sole source of nitrogen; and higher animals can derive a major portion of their protein nitrogen from ammonium salts. The latter must also be supplied with certain essential amino acids.

Ammonia is not the only inorganic substance, however, that can serve as a source of nitrogen. Higher plants readily utilize nitrate ions, while certain microorganisms can even transform molecular nitrogen from the atmosphere into inorganic and organic nitrogen compounds. The process of converting free nitrogen gas to bound nitrogen is known as "nitrogen fixation."

The biological fixation of nitrogen is accomplished by either free-living or symbiotic microorganisms. The former group includes aerobic soil bacteria such as *Azotobacter,* some blue-green algae, photosynthetic bacteria, and the anaerobic *Clostridia.* The symbiotic nitrogen fixers (*Rhizobia*) infect the root hairs of certain kinds of plants, notably legumes such as clover, alfalfa, and soy beans, and grow and multiply in nodules. Neither the plant nor the bacteria can fix nitrogen when grown separately. The nodules contain a pigment related to hemoglobin which has been implicated in the nitrogen fixation reaction.

Very little is known about the details of nitrogen fixation, but one of the early products is ammonia, which, however, does not accumulate. In *Azotobacter* ammonia is utilized as the chief nitrogen source for growth and is thought to be first incorporated into glutamic acid by reaction (2), (see p. 58) and then passed on to other amino acids by transamination (reaction(4)).

Ammonia can also be oxidized readily by two groups of autotrophic bacteria. One, *Nitrosomonas,* converts ammonia to nitrite, while the other group, *Nitrobacter,* then oxidizes the nitrite to nitrate.

$$NH_3 \xrightarrow{\text{Nitrosomonas}} NO_2^- \xrightarrow{\text{Nitrobacter}} NO_3^-$$

Both these reactions are accompanied by the liberation of energy which is used by the bacteria to convert CO_2 to carbohydrate and other carbon compounds. Although microorganisms and the higher plants can accumulate large amounts of nitrate which, unlike ammonia, is relatively nontoxic, they must first reduce it to ammonia before they can assimilate it into cell protein.

Many bacteria, e.g., *Pseudomonas denitrificans,* are able to convert nitrate to N_2 which is thus returned to the atmosphere. This *denitrification* reaction completes the "nitrogen cycle."

■ PHOTOSYNTHESIS

The assimilation of carbon dioxide in green plants by *photosynthesis* is the most important process on this planet for the maintenance of life. All living organisms, with the exception of certain bacteria, derive their energy directly or indirectly from this reaction in which light quanta are absorbed by chlorophyll pigments and transformed by cells into chemical energy for the synthesis of carbohydrates and other organic compounds. Over 85 per cent of the total world photosynthesis takes place in the oceans where it is carried out mainly by marine algae.

The photosynthetic process can be represented as a reversal of respiration:

$$6CO_2 + 6H_2O \longrightarrow C_6H_{12}O_6 + 6O_2; \Delta F = +686,000 \text{ cal}$$

However, the actual sequence of reactions is very complex and can be divided arbitrarily into "light" and "dark" reactions. Light is required for the photochemical decomposition (photolysis) of water into hydrogen and oxygen and also for *photophosphorylation* by which ATP is formed in a manner resembling oxidative phosphorylation. Both mitochondria and chloroplasts contain highly ordered enzyme systems; these allow an exergonic process, such as electron transport through various redox systems, to be coupled with the endergonic

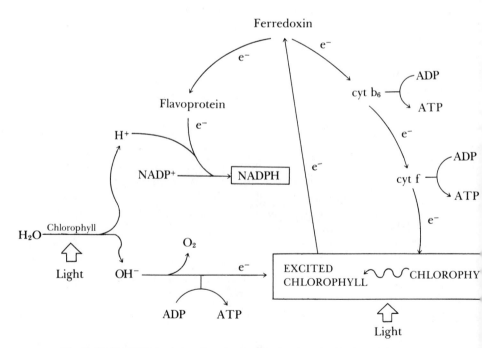

Fig. 3–10. Simplified scheme for photosynthetic phosphorylation and electron transport.

formation of ATP from ADP and inorganic phosphate. After these initial events, the fixation of CO_2 and its conversion to carbohydrate are biochemical reactions which can proceed entirely in the dark.

In photophosphorylation, light quanta are absorbed by the chlorophyll molecule which raises the electrons in this green pigment to a higher energy level. Two types of chlorophyll (a and b) are present in green plants, and these are excited by light of different wave lengths during photosynthesis. Daniel I. Arnon at Berkeley has shown that the high-energy electrons are transferred then to an iron-containing protein, *ferredoxin*, and that photophosphorylation with the production of ATP occurs when the excited electrons return to chlorophyll by way of the intermediate carriers, cytochrome b_6 and cytochrome f (*Fig. 3–10*). Plastoquinone (related to coenzyme Q) may also be involved in this electron transfer.

Isolated chloroplasts also are able to utilize light energy to split water molecules, and the excited electrons that are produced from the hydroxyl ions can be used then to generate ATP. The resulting hydroxy radicals interact immediately to form oxygen which is subsequently eliminated by the plant into the atmosphere. In addition, electrons from ferredoxin may be passed on to a flavoprotein which in turn reduces NADP.

$$2H_2O \xrightarrow{\text{Light}} 2OH^- + 2H^+$$
$$2OH^- \longrightarrow \tfrac{1}{2}O_2 + H_2O + 2e^-$$

$$NADP^+ + 2e^- + 2H^+ \longrightarrow NADPH + H^+ + \tfrac{1}{2}O_2$$

Overall: $H_2O + NADP^+ \xrightarrow{\text{Light}} NADPH + H^+ + \tfrac{1}{2}O_2$

Proof of the photolytic cleavage of water during photosynthesis was provided by M. D. Kamen. Using $H_2{}^{18}O$ he showed that the evolved oxygen contained the heavy isotope ^{18}O. Between five and ten quanta of red light are required per molecule of oxygen liberated by photolysis, but there is still some controversy about this *quantum yield*.

The light induced cleavage of water by isolated chloroplasts was studied first by R. Hill at Cambridge. Although this reaction can result in the formation of ATP, its primary function is to provide the reducing agent ($NADPH_2$) needed for carbon dioxide fixation.

The series of reactions (which can occur equally well in the dark) whereby CO_2 is converted eventually to carbohydrate and other organic compounds has been studied extensively by Melvin Calvin and his associates. Using suspensions of algae, they showed that after

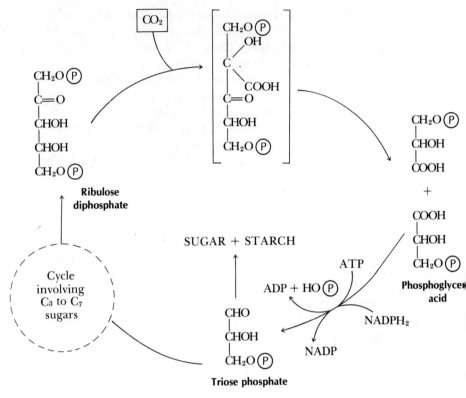

Fig. 3–11. The photosynthetic formation of carbohydrate by the Calvin cycle.

only five seconds of exposure to radioactive CO_2, an appreciable amount of ^{14}C was present in the carboxyl group of 3-phosphoglyceric acid.

$$^{14}COOH$$
$$H—C—OH$$
$$CH_2O\,\text{(P)}$$

However, the primary acceptor of CO_2 is not a 2-carbon compound but rather a pentose, ribulose-1,5-diphosphate which is then cleaved to yield two molecules of 3-phosphoglyceric acid (*Fig. 3–11*). This last compound is reduced by the $NADPH_2$ generated during the light reaction to triose phosphate; a source of energy in the form of ATP is also required. Triose phosphate is then converted to glucose and polysaccharides by a cyclic process having features in common with the reverse of the pentose phosphate pathway.

The cycle, named after Calvin, has been shown to operate in the dark even in a chloroplast-free system, if it contains the appropriate enzymes; of course, the activity of this reconstituted system is not as great as the process in the living plant.

Questions that can be asked about photosynthesis are numerous: Are any of the photosynthetic organisms that are living today similar to the first autotrophs? In what sequence did the various evolutionary changes occur to produce the elaborate photosynthetic system that we see today? What is the detailed mechanism of light capture, and how is it influenced by the molecular organization of the chloroplast? How is ATP generated during photophosphorylation? These are all fundamental problems that demand answers.

1. E. Baldwin, *Dynamic Aspects of Biochemistry*, 4th ed. (Cambridge: Cambridge University Press, 1963), p. 396.
2. H. A. Krebs and W. A. Johnson, "The Role of Citric Acid in Intermediary Metabolism," *Enzymologia*, 4 (1937), 151–152.
3. A. L. Lehninger, *The Mitochondrion: Molecular Basis of Structure and Function* (New York: W. A. Benjamin, Inc., 1964), p. 103.
4. J. Needham, in E. Baldwin, *Dynamic Aspects of Biochemistry*, 4th ed. (Cambridge: Cambridge University Press, 1963), p. 309.

CHAPTER 4 ■ Energy-Requiring
Multienzyme Systems

All organisms do work of one kind or another to remain alive, and basically they carry out three types of energy-requiring reactions: chemical, mechanical, and osmotic work.

The biosynthesis of large, complex cell components, such as proteins, nucleic acids, lipids, and polysaccharides, requires an input of energy, since the assembly of a large complex structure from randomly disposed units results in a decrease in entropy. The contraction of muscle and the movement of structures such as flagella and cilia also require chemical energy, as does the concentration and transport of substances required by the cell. Some of these energy-requiring phenomena will now be considered.

■ THE BIOSYNTHESIS OF MACROMOLECULES

The role of ATP in energy transfer reactions has been mentioned already (Chap. 2), and it must be stressed that the only way in which energy can be transferred from one chemical reaction to another is for the two reactions to have a common intermediate which links them. Thus in the biosynthesis of sucrose by some bacteria (*Pseudomonas saccharophilia*) glucose-1-phosphate acts as such an intermediate:

$$\text{ATP} + \text{Glucose} \longrightarrow \text{ADP} + \text{Glucose-1-}\textcircled{P}$$
$$\text{Glucose-1-}\textcircled{P} + \text{Fructose} \longrightarrow \text{Sucrose} + \text{HO}\textcircled{P}$$

Sum: Glucose + Fructose + ATP $\longrightarrow$

$$\text{Sucrose} + \text{ADP} + \text{HO}\textcircled{P} \;\; \Delta F = -1500 \text{ cal}$$

However, in many biosynthetic reactions in which ATP provides the driving force, the two terminal phosphate groups are removed in one piece as pyrophosphate with the formation of AMP rather than ADP as the end product. Although the free energy change is about the same for both these reactions involving ATP, any released pyrophosphate can be hydrolyzed to orthophosphate by the enzyme pyrophosphatase with a further large decrease in free energy ($\Delta F =$ -7000 cal). This provides an additional thermodynamic "pull" for synthetic reactions.

Other nucleoside triphosphates (CTP, GTP and UTP) have about the same free energy of hydrolysis of the terminal phosphate group as ATP and act as energy carriers for specific reactions. However, they are all synthesized by reactions involving ATP which, therefore, ultimately provides the phosphate group for all biosynthetic processes.

Lehninger has calculated the turnover rate of ATP during active biosynthesis of the major cell components in *E. coli* and has shown that each phospholipid molecule requires eight molecules of ATP, each polysaccharide molecule about 2000, each protein molecule about 1500, each RNA molecule about 6000, and each DNA molecule about 120,000,000 molecules of ATP per second for its biosynthesis. A minimum of 2,500,000 molecules of ATP are broken down per second in order to achieve the biosynthesis of all the cell components. Since the whole bacterium contains only about one million molecules of ATP, this compound must be regenerated very rapidly from ADP and inorganic phosphate. This is achieved by oxidative phosphorylation (Chap. 3).

■ BIOSYNTHESIS OF POLYSACCHARIDES

The polysaccharides consist of long chains of simple sugar molecules joined in glycosidic (ether-type) linkage. The polysaccharides may be divided into two main functional classes: one group, such as cellulose, acts as structural material; while another group, which includes glycogen in animals and starch in plants, serves as a store of monosaccharides.

It is now believed that the formation of polysaccharides from glucose-1-phosphate by the glycogen phosphorylase reaction (Chap. 3) is not a normal physiological process, and that phosphorylases act mainly as degradative enzymes. It is a general biological principle that synthetic pathways differ at some point from the reverse of the degradative pathways. This is of importance in the control of metabolic reactions (Chap. 5).

The synthesis of glycogen (*Fig. 4–1*) illustrates the mechanism involved in the biosynthesis of most polysaccharides:

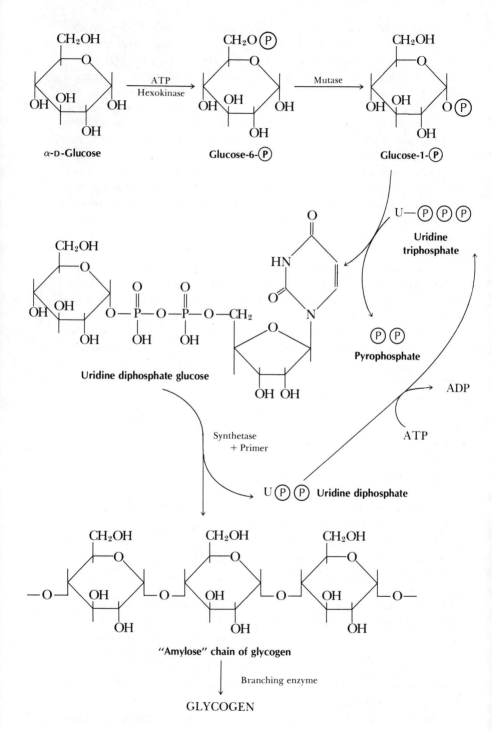

Fig. 4–1. The biosynthesis of glycogen.

Glucose is phosphorylated to glucose-6-phosphate to raise its energy content; it is then converted to glucose-1-phosphate which in turn reacts with uridine triphosphate to form uridine diphosphate glucose (UDP-glucose). This last product, which serves as a glucose carrier, was shown by L. F. Leloir to act by transferring its glucose component to an existing gylcogen chain thus lengthening it by one unit. Glycogen synthetase, the enzyme which catalyzes this reaction, cannot alone form glucose from UDP-glucose; it requires an acceptor polyglucose chain. This *"primer,"* however, can be very much smaller than the normally occurring glycogen molecule, and even maltose can serve as an acceptor, though at a very low rate. If the reaction started with maltose, it would be very slow at the beginning but would become gradually faster as larger acceptors were formed.

A straight chain α-1,4-linked polymer of glucose (amylose) thus is added to the primer by repeated addition of glucose units; but, in order to produce branching, another enzyme is needed. This "branching" enzyme catalyzes the formation of α-1,6 linkages and acts by transferring whole segments of α-1,4-linked glucose units to the 6-hydroxyl group of a glucose residue elsewhere in the chain, as shown in *Fig. 4-2.*

From the thermodynamic point of view, nucleoside diphosphate sugars, such as UDP-glucose, have a better glucosyl transfer potential than other glucose donors. It has been shown recently that nucleosides other than uridine also are involved in carbohydrate metabolism. Thus plants synthesize starch from ADP-glucose, cellulose from GDP-glucose (guanosine diphosphate glucose); and it now appears that virtually all polysaccharides are built up from small units by the reaction pattern described above.

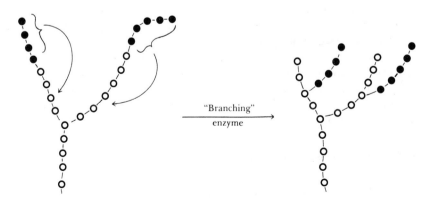

Fig. 4-2. Action of "branching" enzyme in the synthesis of glycogen. α-1,4-linked glucose molecules ● are transferred in one piece.

■ BIOSYNTHESIS OF LIPIDS

The lipids as a class generally are not considered to be macromolecules, since their molecular weights rarely exceed 1000; but they are of interest from the energy storage viewpoint and also because phospholipids are important components of the cell membrane.

The biosynthesis of phosphatidyl choline (lecithin), which is the most widespread of the phospholipids in nature, shows some similarities to the biosynthesis of polysaccharides. Thus it requires activation of its building blocks by ATP-linked reactions and utilizes a nucleoside diphosphate derivative, CDP-choline, as specific carrier. Both fats (triglycerides) and phospholipids have identical biosynthetic pathways as far as diglyceride (*Fig. 4–3*), although some alternative routes for the synthesis of phospholipids are also known.

■ BIOSYNTHESIS OF INFORMATIONAL MACROMOLECULES

The polysaccharides and lipid molecules, although very important in cell structure and function, are not concerned primarily with the handling of cellular information. This is carried out by two groups of macromolecules, the nucleic acids which are adapted for the *storage* and *transcription* of biological information and the proteins which are responsible for the *expression* of this information.

The information content of protein and nucleic acid molecules can be calculated by using information theory, an extension of thermodynamics and probability theory; and the unit used is the *bit* (binary digit). Thus it has been calculated that proteins contain more bits of information per unit weight than the DNA molecules which act as code for them. This is reasonable, since three mononucleotide units are required to code each amino acid (discussed later); but, in addition, the specific amino acid coded by each triplet may have more than "meaning" in protein structure and may function differently depending on its position in the peptide chain.

The biosynthesis of nucleic acids and proteins necessarily is more complex than that of the polysaccharides and lipids, because the building block molecules must be put together in the exact and specific sequence required for the full biological function of these informational macromolecules.

■ THE REPLICATION OF DNA

The information stored in any molecule that acts as the genetic material must be passed on with great accuracy from generation to generation; and, if this information indeed is contained in the se-

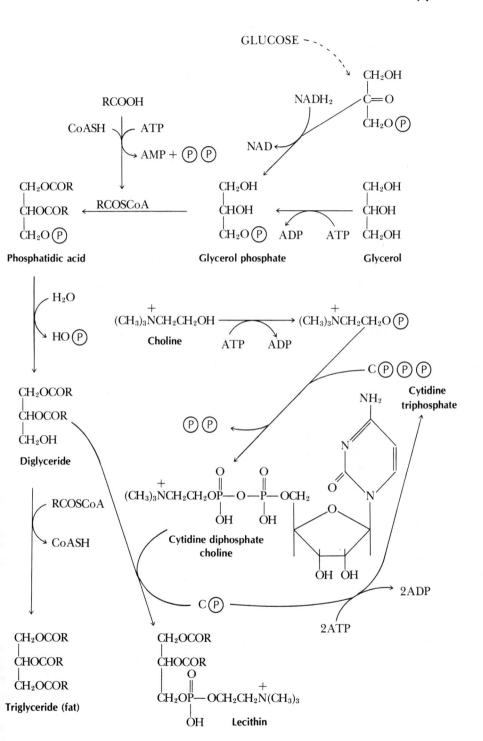

Fig. 4–3. The biosynthesis of triglyceride and a phospholipid (lecithin).

quence of bases of DNA, this sequence must be kept intact. There is now strong evidence that this is the case; and that the two original strands of the DNA helix, which were held together by hydrogen bonds between specific pairs of bases (adenine with thymine, guanine with cytosine), separate but remain intact, each acting as template for a new DNA strand. At the end of this process, which is said to be "semiconservative," two hybrid daughter helices are formed, each consisting of one old and one new DNA chain with the bases paired in complementary fashion according to the Watson-Crick model (see Vol. I).

The synthesis of a new strand of DNA which is structurally complementary to the inherited single-stranded DNA is called *replication* and is catalyzed by the enzyme DNA polymerase. The reaction involves the deoxynucleoside triphosphates of adenine, guanine, cytosine, and thymine, a DNA molecule to act as template, and Mg^{++} ions (*Fig. 4–4*).

This enzymatic replication reaction generally proceeds only if single-stranded template DNA is present, together with all four of the deoxynucleoside triphosphates. However, in certain cases DNA polymerase can synthesize a special DNA without any template being present, but only after a long lag period. Thus if given only the adenine and thymine precursors, it will produce a polymer having a strictly alternating base sequence and a base-paired double helical structure. If the precursors are guanine and cytosine, it will synthesize chains of two types, either all guanine or all cytosine; and these two homopolymers then form a double helix with each other.

During the synthesis of DNA, one molecule of pyrophosphate is formed for each mononucleotide subunit incorporated into the chain and is then hydrolyzed by pyrophosphatase with a large decrease in free energy. The exact replication of DNA is also helped by another thermodynamic driving force which in the words of Lehninger

> . . . is imparted by the "fit" of the newly formed DNA strand to the preexisting DNA template strand. Each base in the template allows only its complementary base to fit with it in the double-helical arrangement; all other pairings of the bases are excluded because they do not fit the double-helical structure. When a mononucleotide is added whose base fits the corresponding base in the template, the double-helix stabilizes itself and the reaction is "pulled" further towards completion. This stabilization force or thermodynamic pull increases with the chain length of the DNA. Thus the faithful replication of DNA is guaranteed by the operation of fundamental thermodynamic principles. The specific geometrical relationship between the enzyme molecule, the single-stranded template and the double-helical product of the polymerase are not yet known, but they offer an exciting challenge.[1]

Exactly how the two chains of the double helix of DNA unwind during replication is yet another problem, and it would be of interest to know how this is achieved for such extremely long molecules, how the energy is supplied, and how this is done in a neat and systematic manner. It is remarkable that the two daughter molecules can come apart into separate regions without getting hopelessly entangled. It appears that synthesis and unwinding go on together, so that only a small part of the chain near the growing point is ever single stranded at any one time (*Fig. 4–5*). The rate of synthesis of DNA is very high; it has been estimated that in some bacteria it may proceed at the rate of 3000 base pairs per second.

■ TRANSCRIPTION AND THE BIOSYNTHESIS OF RNA

The transcription of the information embodied in the specific sequence of bases in the DNA molecule proceeds by an enzymatic reaction that is analogous to that occurring during replication. Thus in the presence of DNA and Mg^{++} ions, a specific polymerase catalyzes the assembly of the nucleoside triphosphates of adenine, guanine, cytosine, and uracil into a type of RNA known as messenger RNA (mRNA), a term descriptive of its role as the carrier of the genetic "message" from the nucleus to the sites of protein synthesis in the cytoplasm.

Although double stranded DNA is used normally for transcription, only one of the strands is copied, with the result that the mRNA

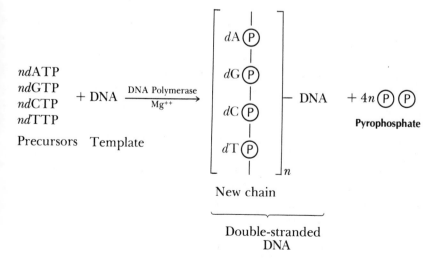

Fig. 4–4. The biosynthesis of DNA.

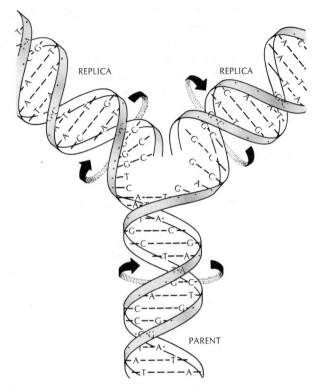

Fig. 4-5. Replication of DNA, according to the mechanism of Watson and Crick. (From G. S. Stent, *Molecular Biology of Bacterial Viruses*, W. H. Freeman and Co.)

formed has the same base sequence (with uracil in place of thymine) as the unused DNA strand. This was demonstrated first by J. J. Furth, Jerrard Hurwitz, and M. Goldman who used as template synthetic poly dAT, in which A and T alternated with one another along the DNA chain. They showed that the RNA produced by RNA polymerase was poly AU, in which A and U alternated with one another along the RNA chain.

Transcription occurs within the minor groove (see Vol. I) of the DNA double helix. The evidence for this is provided by the findings that the antibiotic actinomycin D, which specifically binds to the guanine residues in the minor groove of DNA, completely inhibits RNA synthesis without affecting DNA replication.*

---

*Significantly, actinomycin D has no effect on the cellular replication of RNA viruses, which implies that viral RNA serves as its own template and does not require DNA. The RNA also acts as messenger for the synthesis of virus specific enzymes (including RNA polymerase) and virus proteins by the host cell ribosomes.

In this way a complementary hybrid molecule of DNA and RNA is formed. It then unwinds by a mechanism that yet is not understood, and the single strand of messenger RNA then leaves the nucleus to diffuse into the endoplasmic reticulum. Here it becomes attached to the ribosomes and strings them together into polysomes (discussed later). In bacterial cells, the turnover of mRNA is very rapid, but in most mammalian cells it is very much slower.

The DNA-dependent RNA polymerase catalyzing the formation of mRNA is universally distributed and generally is found in the nuclei associated with chromosomal DNA. It is actually possible to follow RNA synthesis on the active genes in the giant salivary chromosomes of the fruit fly *Drosophila* or the midge *Chironomus* by the appearance of swellings known as puffs (*Fig. 4–7*). The induction of puffing can be prevented by actinomycin D.

RNA polymerase also is believed to catalyze the formation of two other types of ribonucleic acid — *ribosomal RNA* (rRNA), which is the major RNA component of the cell; and *soluble RNA* (sRNA), also known as *transfer RNA* (tRNA), which in most cells accounts for between 10 and 15 per cent of the total RNA. Whereas both mRNA and rRNA are large macromolecules with molecular weights around one million, sRNA has a molecular weight of only about 25,000 and is composed of approximately 80 nucleotides. Robert W. Holley and his group at Cornell University now have determined the complete

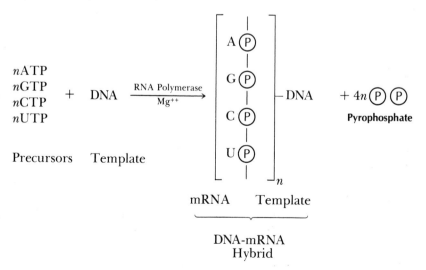

Fig. 4–6. Biosynthesis of messenger RNA (transcription).

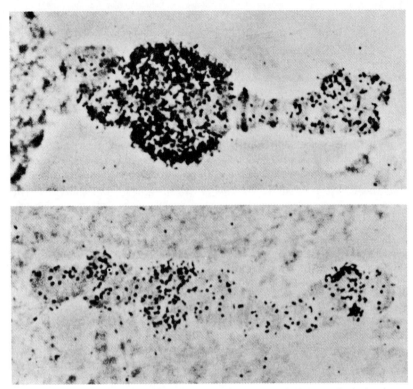

Fig. 4-7. Chromosome puffs. Inhibition of puffing and of RNA synthesis is accomplished by treatment with the antibiotic actinomycin D. At top an autoradiogram of a chromosome IV of *Ch. tentans* shows the incorporation of much radioactive uridine *(black spots)*, which takes place during the production of RNA, as explained in the text. Another chromosome IV *(bottom)* that had been puffing shows puff regression and little radioactivity after half an hour of treatment with minute amounts of actinomycin D, which inhibits RNA synthesis by DNA. (From W. Beermann and U. Clever, "Chromosome Puffs." Copyright © 1964 by Scientific American, Inc. All rights reserved.)

nucleotide sequence of yeast alanine-transfer RNA which thus becomes the first nucleic acid for which the structure is known. More recently the nucleotide sequence in yeast tyrosine-transfer RNA also has been elucidated.

The function of rRNA in the ribosomes is still a mystery, and a structural role has been assigned to it provisionally. However, the function of sRNA is understood fairly well. It is now recognized that the molecule acts as an acceptor for an activated amino acid and as an "adaptor" for carrying the amino acid to the site of protein synthesis (see below). It ensures that the correct amino acid is placed on the correct coding site, and for each of the 20 naturally occurring amino acids there is at least one specific type of sRNA molecule.

Soluble RNA also differs from the rest of cellular RNA in containing small quantities of some unusual nucleotides (pseudouridylic acid and ribothymidilic acid); and, in addition, each sRNA molecule has a terminal nucleotide base sequence of —CCA. These last three nucleotides are added not by the nuclear polymerase but sequentially by a special enzyme system located in the cytoplasm of the cell. The other end of the sRNA chain, which does not accept amino acids, is always guanylic acid; and, even though there is only one chain, most of the bases are hydrogen bonded to each other by complementary base pairing. This is accomplished by "hairpin" folds that bring bases on the same chain into a DNA-like double-helical arrangement.

Although all these forms of RNA are produced in the nucleus, the possibility that some cytoplasmic synthesis of RNA also may be occurring cannot be excluded. As a matter of fact, it has been shown that the nucleus of the alga, *Acetabularia,* can be removed without completely abolishing the synthesis of RNA in this organism.

An RNA-dependent RNA polymerase has been demonstrated in certain bacteria and viruses; and, in addition, it has been found that RNA polymerase copies only one of the DNA chains in the cell but usually copies both of them if the reaction is carried out in the test tube. This emphasizes the caution that must be used in extending *in vitro* results to the *in vivo* situation.

The reason why nature should have chosen nucleic acid rather than protein to carry the genetic information of the cell is elegantly discussed by F. H. C. Crick:

As far as we know, nucleic acid has only two major functions. It can serve as a template for the replication of more nucleic acid or it can direct protein synthesis by acting as mRNA. No authentic case of nucleic acid acting as an enzyme has yet been discovered.

Proteins, on the other hand, are as a class immensely versatile. Every biochemist knows that all known enzymes are proteins. What protein apparently cannot do easily is to form a regular double helix suitable for a simple replication mechanism. Nevertheless, it is not too difficult to imagine a rather complicated system which could replicate protein. I am not completely clear why this has not occurred (for there is certainly no evidence for it). It may be that there are theoretical reasons why one type of molecule should act as the genetic material, of which basically only one copy is required, and another type should act as enzymes, many copies of which are needed. Then again, the action of proteins demands that they form a relatively stable three-dimensional structure. To be copied this would have to be unfolded. Whatever the reason, Nature has found it better to make nucleic acid the genetic material, although this means that very elaborate biochemical machinery is needed in order that it can direct

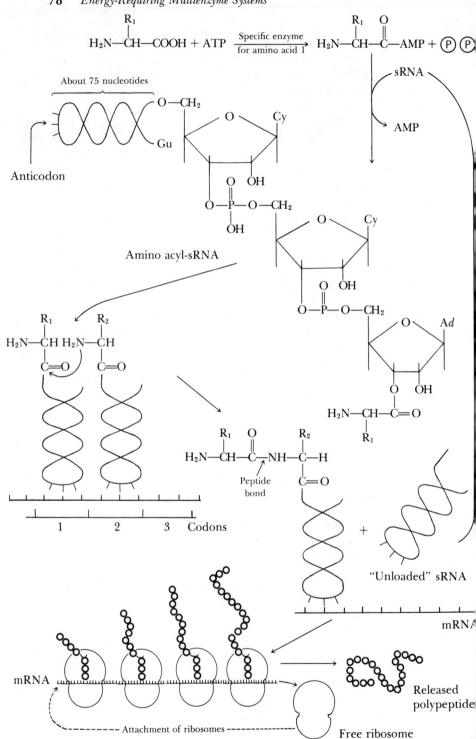

Fig. 4–8. Amino acid activation and protein synthesis.

protein synthesis. It is not easy to see how this could have arisen. It must have evolved by successive stages.[2]

■ PROTEIN BIOSYNTHESIS

The genetic information of the cell is expressed through the synthesis of protein. This process, which utilizes about 90 per cent of the cell's biosynthetic energy, is probably the most fundamental activity of living organisms. The mechanism is complex and occurs on the ribosomes of the endoplasmic reticulum after the amino acids have combined with sRNA.

Each of the amino acids undergoes activation in the presence of ATP and a specific amino acid activating enzyme to form an amino acyl-AMP intermediate. This activated enzyme-bound complex then transfers the amino acyl moiety to the 3′-hydroxyl group of the terminal adenosine of sRNA (*Fig. 4–8*). Each amino acid has its own set of sRNA molecules containing a specific triplet of nucleotides (anticodon) which forms base pairs with the complementary triplet (codon) in the mRNA associated with the ribosomes. One mRNA molecule may bind several (often five) ribosomes, and such clusters held together by a long strand of mRNA are called *polyribosomes* or *polysomes.*

The base sequence along the mRNA molecule, which is an exact replica of that in one of the strands of nuclear DNA, determines the sequence of amino acids to be inserted. Three adjacent nucleotide residues on the mRNA chain are needed to code for each amino acid. Such a coding triplet is known as a *codon.* The succession of triplets along the nucleotide chain is believed to be nonoverlapping—that is, nucleotides one, two, and three specify the first amino acid; four, five, and six the second, etc.; and it is also "commaless." Thus if during mutation a single nucleotide is added or lost, the reading frame is completely upset, and the polypeptide product will have no biological activity.

Furthermore, treatment of viruses with nitrous acid, which converts the cytosine base in RNA to uracil and adenine to guanine, also has helped to elucidate the genetic code, since, under these circumstances, certain amino acids of the proteins in the virus coat become replaced by others.

Both natural and artificial polyribonucleotides can substitute for endogenous mRNA in the *in vitro* synthesizing system; and, in this way, as well as by binding studies with specific nucleotide triplets, the codons for all the common amino acids have been deduced (Table 4–1). Thus M. W. Nirenberg has been able to show, for example, that the trinucleotide GUU promotes the bindings of the sRNA for valine to ribosomes, whereas UGU and UUG does not. More recently,

TABLE 4–1

The Genetic Code[a]

First Base	Second Base				Third Base
	U	C	A	G	
U	PHE	SER	TYR	CYS	U
	PHE	SER	TYR	CYS	C
	LEU	SER	"ochre"*	?	A
	LEU	SER	"amber"*	TRY	G
C	LEU	PRO	HIS	(arg)	U
	LEU	PRO	HIS	ARG	C
	?	PRO	GLUN	ARG	A
	(leu)	PRO	GLUN	ARG	G
A	ILEU	THR	ASPN	SER	U
	ILEU	THR	ASPN	(ser)	C
	Ileu?	THR	LYS	ARG	A
	MET	THR	LYS	?	G
G	VAL	ALA	ASP	GLY	U
	VAL	ALA	ASP	GLY	C
	VAL	ALA	GLU	GLY	A
	VAL	ALA	GLU	GLY	G

A:	Adenine	GLUN:	Glutamine	MET:	Methionine
G:	Guanine	GLY:	Glycine	PHE:	Phenylalanine
ALA:	Alanine	HIS:	Histidine	PRO:	Proline
ARG:	Arginine	ILEU:	Isoleucine	SER:	Serine
ASP:	Aspartic acid	C:	Cytosine	THR:	Threonine
ASPN:	Asparagine	U:	Uracil	TRY:	Tryptophan
CYS:	Cysteine	LEU:	Leucine	TYR:	Tyrosine
GLU:	Glutamic acid	LYS:	Lysine	VAL:	Valine

* Cause chain termination.
[a] Courtesy A. O. W. Stretton, "The Genetic Code," *British Medical Bulletin*, 21 (1965), 229.

H. G. Khorana at Wisconsin has made available all 64 of the possible nucleotide triplets for testing the genetic code. He also has synthesized several repeating nucleotide polymers of considerable length.

The ribosomes are constructed from two subunits, a larger one which contains two binding sites for amino acyl-sRNA, and a smaller one to which mRNA is attached. When the amino acid has become fixed in position by highly specific bonding between the anticodon of sRNA and the codon of mRNA, it forms a peptide bond with the carboxyl end of the peptide chain next to it. This enzymatic reaction requires the participation of GTP and is accompanied by release of the now "empty" molecule of sRNA. The true function of GTP is not understood at all. One suggestion has been that it provides energy to move the ribosomes along the strand of mRNA. When the polypeptide chain is synthesized fully, it must be released from the ribosomes. It is believed that nonsense signals are set aside in the code to prevent the extension of polypeptide chains beyond certain points. The triplet sequence UAA may be one such chain terminator. There is also evidence that formyl methionine may be put in at the beginning of the growing chain and the formyl group then removed.

Once the amino acid has been attached to its specific sRNA, its future fate is decided by the coding properties of its sRNA adaptor (anticodon). This was shown by some ingenious experiments carried out jointly by groups at Rockefeller, Johns Hopkins, and Purdue Universities. The plan of the experiments is illustrated below (*Fig. 4–9*).

Cysteine was attached to its normal acceptor sRNA through the mediation of the cysteine activating enzyme. By the action of finely-divided nickel, the cysteine while still attached was converted to alanine. The coding properties of the hybrid molecules were then investigated, and it was found that the resultant alanyl-sRNA was incorporated into polypeptide by a system which normally incorporates cysteine but not alanine. Since an amino acid, once attached, no longer participates in coding, it was concluded that the code is embodied in the precise structures and interrelationships of the set of sRNA anticodons and activating enzymes.

In another experiment, G. von Ehrenstein and F. Lipmann showed that sRNA from one species may be used to synthesize a protein typical of a different species. Thus rabbit reticulocyte polysomes containing mRNA for hemoglobin synthesized this protein when sRNA from *E. coli*, previously charged with amino acids using *E. coli* activating enzyme, was used.

The antibiotic *puromycin*, which has a chemical structure resembling that of the terminal part of amino acyl-sRNA inhibits the transfer of amino acids into the growing polypeptide chain in the ribosomes and causes the release of incomplete polypeptide chains. The experi-

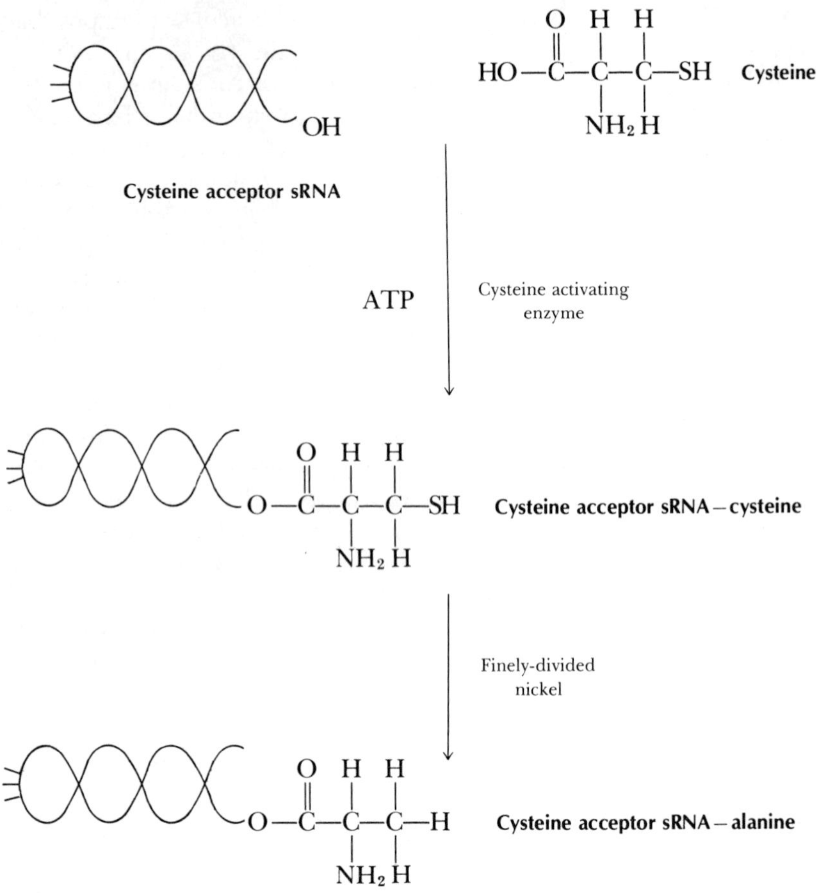

Fig. 4–9. Chemical conversion of sRNA – cysteine to sRNA – alanine.

mental evidence suggests that the genetic code is universal whereas the relationship between an sRNA molecule and the activating enzyme is often species specific. In the words of Crick:

> If the meaning of the triplet is changed, most of the genes in the organism will be affected, and the change is almost certain to be lethal. Thus, the code will never change once organisms have reached a certain minimum size. On the other hand to change the relationship between an sRNA and its activating enzyme only a few simultaneous changes might be needed, some on the gene which controls the sRNA and some compensating change on the gene for the activating enzyme. Over very long periods of time we might very well expect a drift of this sort to occur.

This argument leaves open the possibility that at an early stage in the evolution of the code there may have been some special relationship between a few of the amino acids and certain base sequences on the nucleic acid. It merely states that once an arbitrary (or partly arbitrary) code has arisen, it may be difficult to alter, although parts of the coding machinery may change nevertheless.[3]

He summarizes by saying:

The general scheme we have been considering for gene structure, gene replication and gene action appears to be basically the same throughout nature. It combines simplicity with complexity in a striking and characteristic manner. The device of carrying the genetic information on a polymer, using a language of four side-groups is one of great power and elegance. The information is carried on a one-dimensional structure. The existence of the two base-pairs allows the genetic replication to be accompanied in a simple manner.

Complexity appears with proteins. They are necessarily complex because proteins, as a class, need to carry out many different functions, both enzymatic and structural, and Natural Selection has refined them so that they do so with great precision. Their elaborate structure is achieved by the way each protein folds up to form its unique three-dimensional conformation. Nevertheless, the underlying chemical plan is simple: that of twenty standard units, the amino acids, joined up in a uniform manner into polypeptide chains. However, they must be joined up in the correct sequence, and rather elaborate biochemical machinery is needed to enable the nucleic acid to direct this. The whole arrangement provides an immensely powerful instrument by which Natural Selection can operate. Allowing for the necessary limitations of macromolecular structure, it may well be the best that could be devised.[3]

■ THE CONVERSION OF CHEMICAL ENERGY INTO WORK

So far we have seen how the energy of glycolysis and respiration, as well as that of sunlight, is conserved in the form of ATP. The problem now arises as to how the chemical energy of this molecule is converted into mechanical, osmotic, and electrical work by living cells.

CONTRACTION AND MOTION

In multicellular animals a good deal of the energy trapped in the form of ATP is consumed in the movement of the animal itself. Contractile activity, however, is not limited to muscle cells. Almost all cells show contractile or motile activity of one kind or another, specialized for different purposes; and it just happens that muscle cells, during evolution, have developed an extraordinary ability to contract in one direction. The different types of contractile systems found in nature are aptly described by Lehninger:

> Contractile fibers or sheets located in the cytoplasm or in cell membranes participate in many aspects of cellular activity. During mitosis or cell division, contractile fibers in the cytoplasm aid in pulling apart the chromosomal material of the nucleus into two zones. Contractile elements in the cytoplasm also aid in separating the parent cell into its two progeny. Contractile fibers are also important in the structural development of cells during differentiation. Furthermore, the cell membrane and the membrane of the nucleus may undergo contraction and relaxation that lead to changes in shape or volume. Recent research indicates that mitochondria as well as chloroplasts also undergo swelling-contraction cycles that are directly linked to electron transport and coupled phosphorylation of ADP. Presumably, their membranes contain contractile elements; in fact, a contractile protein very similar to that in muscle has been found in mitochondria.
>
> There are other types of mechanochemical systems in cells which participate in motility or propulsion. The locomotion of amoebae is caused by contractile processes in the cytoplasm and membrane. Paramecia have contractile structures in their plasma membrane called *trichocysts*, which are forcibly ejected from the cell surface; presumably they are devices to unload or secrete waste products. Other cells such as spermatozoa, possess *flagella* which carry out two-dimensional "whiplash" movements used for propulsion. Still other cells have *cilia*, which are used to move materials past them. All these structures have biochemical properties that are similar to those of muscle in one way or another.
>
> The most highly developed and most studied contractile system are those of muscle cells, but even here these are large biological variations in structure and function. At one extreme of physiological specialization are the flight muscles of flying insects, which perform mechanical work at enormously high rates; they may have contraction—relaxation cycles of a frequency as high as 1000 per second and are turned on and off with essentially no lag period. At the other extreme, the skeletal muscle of the tortoise contracts and relaxes slowly; it is also slow to get moving and slow to stop. Heart muscle is another specialized type; it has the property of precise and automatic contraction and relaxation. Smooth or involuntary muscle, as in the intestine, has a slow, generalized contractile action. Still other muscles can apply sustained tension for extremely long periods, as though they can "lock"; an example is the adductor muscle of the clam, which can literally lock itself in the contracted state.[4]

All these different types of contractile systems appear to possess the same basic kind of molecular engine to convert the chemical energy of ATP into mechanical energy. They require the specific interaction of two macromolecules, *actin* and *myosin*. Myosin is a long, thin protein (1500 Å × 20 Å) with a molecular weight of approximately 350,000. It can be split by the enzyme trypsin into two well-defined fragments, *light meromyosin* and *heavy meromyosin*. The ability to split ATP and to combine with actin is controlled by the more globular heavy meromyosin fragment, whereas the general shape and solubility properties of myosin are determined mainly by the light meromyosin component.

Threads of myosin by themselves, however, will not contract in the presence of ATP until another protein, actin, is added to form *actomyosin*. Actin can exist in two forms G-actin (globular form) and F-actin (fibrous form) which are interconvertible. G-actin can be polymerized into the long fibrous form by the addition of ATP, and it is F-actin which then forms a complex with myosin. Thus both the major protein components of the contractile machinery, actin and myosin, can react with ATP, the universal fuel for muscular activity.

It has been found by physicochemical methods that the hydrolysis of ATP to ADP by actomyosin is accompanied by dissociation of this protein complex into actin and myosin. These components then recombine when the ATP is exhausted. The changes in the conformation of actomyosin while it is performing its enzymatic (ATPase) activity results in mechanical changes; and, in fact, contraction can be demonstrated by adding ATP to an artificially-produced thread of actomyosin.

A "sliding" mechanism has been proposed to account for the ultrastructural changes observed with the filaments of myofibrils during contraction. It appears that the molecules of actin and myosin slide into each other in telescopic fashion by making and breaking lateral chemical bonds between them (*Fig. 4-10*). However, the precise molecular events by which the chemical energy of ATP is converted into mechanical energy is still at the speculative stage.

ATP is important not only for contraction but also for relaxation affecting the elastic properties of the muscle. This softening effect of ATP must be distinguished from the physiological *relaxing factor* which consists of an enzyme system catalyzing the active transport of calcium ions away from the cytoplasmic space. During this process ATPase activity is inhibited, and the bonds between actin and myosin are split. *Rigor mortis* is believed to be caused by the absence of the relaxing factor, leaving actin and myosin strongly linked together.

Since the activity of muscle is so dependent on ATP, which is present only in small concentrations, it is fortunate that there are relatively large amounts of another high-energy compound, creatine phosphate, in vertebrate muscle (a similar compound, arginine phosphate, exists in invertebrate muscle). This compound under the influence of creatine kinase (Chap. 2) reacts readily and reversibly with ADP to give creatine and ATP.

In the earliest stages of muscular activity, ATP is broken down to supply the energy required; but the residual ADP has no need to wait for the whole metabolic machinery to get under way. Instead it can be converted back at once into ATP (at the expense of its stores of creatine phosphate). The supplies of storage material seem to be calculated nicely to tide the muscle over until its metabolic mills have got well under way and can produce energy and ATP as fast as they are utilized. During rest ATP produced in the usual manner reacts with free creatine to replenish the reserve of creatine phosphate, while the ADP produced is fed back to other metabolic systems for rephosphorylation.

However, because of the rapid regeneration of ATP from creatine phosphate, it took many years to answer the challenge that A. V. Hill issued to biochemists to prove that in living muscle ATP was the immediate energy supply for contraction. This was finally proven in 1962 by D. F. Cain and R. E. Davies who wrote:

> Experiments with isolated enzymes, muscle protein solutions, reconstituted actomyosin fibrils and glycerinated muscle models have suggested that adenosine triphosphate is the immediate source of energy for muscle contraction. However, despite enormous efforts, numerous attempts to demonstrate changes in concentration of ATP during a single contraction cycle have repeatedly shown that no quantitatively sufficient changes occur. This has been interpreted as being due to very rapid regeneration of ATP from phosphorylcreatine

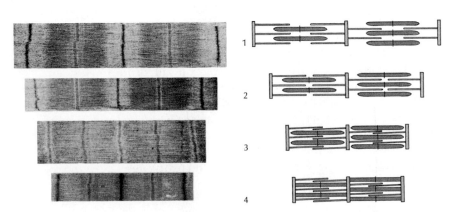

Fig. 4-10. Contraction of muscle entails change in relative position of the thick and thin filaments that comprise the myofibril *(top left and right)*. The effect of contraction on the band pattern of muscle is indicated by four electron micrographs and accompanying schematic illustrations of muscle in longitudinal section, fixed at consecutive stages of contraction. The molecules of actin and myosin slide into each other in telescopic fashion. (From H. E. Huxley, "The Mechanism of Muscular Contraction." Copyright © 1965 by Scientific American, Inc. All rights reserved.)

catalyzed by the enzyme creatine phosphoryl transferase (creatine kinase). Although single contractions of muscle without measurable changes in phosphorylcreatine have been reported, recent results with improved techniques have shown clearly that approximately 0.6 μmole/gm muscle of this compound does in fact break down to form creatine and inorganic phosphate when work is done during a single contraction. . . .

Kuby and Mahowald showed that crystalline creatine phosphoryl transferase is completely inhibited by 1-fluoro-2,4-dinitrobenzene (FDNB) and, using this inhibitor, we have now found the long-sought-for changes in ATP.

After pretreatment of the muscle with FDNB, the number of full, normal contractions which could be performed by an isolated muscle was reduced from more than 30 to about 3, yet these muscles still contained the same amount of phosphorylcreatine as resting, untreated muscle. This communication shows that the energy for these contractions came from the breakdown of ATP.[5]

In spite of the great specialization that muscle has undergone for one purpose or another, the chemical mechanism involved in supplying the energy for contraction has remained fundamentally the same. Throughout the animal kingdom creatine or arginine phosphate are present in smooth, cardiac, and striated muscle. It is present also in the electric organs of fishes such as *Torpedo*, the electric ray, and *Electrophorus,* the electric eel. *Torpedo* is able to deliver electric shocks of the order of 300 volts on open circuit. The cells of its electric organs arise from premuscular tissue in the embryo and are thus like true muscle in many respects. The manner in which these bioelectric generators convert the chemical energy of ATP into electrical energy, as well as the problems of nerve conduction and active transport, are discussed in Vol. VI of this series.

BIOLUMINESCENCE

Many organisms are known to emit light. This phenomenon of *bioluminescence* occurs when the energy released during biological oxidation forces an electron in a molecule to a higher energy level. Although the chemical events in bioluminescence are not understood fully, it appears that one of the biochemical processes involves the oxidation of a member of a group of substances known as *luciferins* by the enzyme luciferase in the presence of ATP and Mg^{++} ions. There is evidence that some of the luciferins may be flavins. Luciferase has been isolated now in crystalline form.

Bioluminescence frequently is called "cold light," because it is a highly efficient energy-transfer process with very little dissipation of heat. The intensity of light produced can be considerable (see Fig.

2–2, Chap. 2) and, in fact, can be used to assay ATP, since it is proportional to the amount of this nucleotide present.

Much of the work on bioluminescence has been carried out with the firefly (*Photinus gyralis*), the crustacean *Cypridina hilgendorfia,* and the marine bacterium, *Achromobacter fischerii.* However, many other organisms also exhibit this phenomenon, including decaying wood fungi, luminous toadstools, protozoa, sponges, jellyfish, snails, the luminous clam (*Pholas dactylus*), shrimps, starfish, flies, centipedes, and the glowworm. The biological value of light emission, as well as its significance during evolution, has been well described by W. D. McElroy, a pioneer in this field:

> A number of investigators have attempted to determine the importance of light emission to those organisms that display this remarkable ability. Unfortunately there is no clear answer as yet. There are many examples in which the bioluminescent reaction has been adapted to good biological use. The reproduction cycles of a number of organisms in the sea are tied to light emission. The flash of the firefly is used by some species as a sex signal. Light emission by deep-sea organisms provides the only light source for those organisms at great depths that have eyes. In some cases luminous bacteria are known to grow in special glands on fish and to provide a regular source of light. Whether light emission in the deeps of the ocean trigger other photobiological processes is not known but it is a safe guess that it does.
>
> That there are many different chemical types of bioluminescent reactions suggests that they arose independently during evolution and are an expression of the reverse process of photosynthesis. In photosynthesis oxygen is evolved and organic molecules are produced by various reduction reactions, whereas in bioluminescence oxygen decomposes organic molecules in an oxidative event that leads to an excited state and light emission. It has been suggested that excited states of this type normally occur in oxidative reactions but the energy is most often used to generate ATP rather than to produce light emission. In fact, one can present a reasonable argument that life arose and evolved by making use of excited states, as plants are capable of doing now in photosynthesis. During the early evolution of life, therefore, many more light-emitting organisms may have existed than we see at the present time. Bioluminescence is perhaps gradually being lost as organisms evolve effective means of utilizing the energy of the excited state. The use of light emission for specific purposes may thus have been secondary in the evolutionary process. Obviously much work remains to be done in this area of biological energy transformation.[6]

1. A. L. Lehninger, *Biogenetics: The Molecular Basis of Energy Transformations* (New York: W. A. Benjamin, Inc., 1965), pp. 210–211.
2. F. H. C. Crick, "The Biochemistry of Genetics," *Proceedings of the Plenary Sessions of the 6th International Congress of Biochemistry*, New York, 1964, p. 109.
3. *Ibid.*, pp. 109–128.
4. Lehninger, *op. cit.*, pp. 136–137.
5. D. F. Cain and R. E. Davies, "Breakdown of Adenosine Triphosphate During a Single Contraction of Working Muscle," *Biochemical and Biophysical Research Communication*, 8 (1962), 361.
6. William D. McElroy, *Cell Physiology and Biochemistry*, 2nd ed, © 1964, pp. 92–93. Reprinted by permission of Prentice-Hall, Inc., Englewood Cliffs, New Jersey.

CHAPTER 5 Control and
Regulation
of Cellular Activity

In the previous chapters reference has been made to the fact that
growth and development, as well as the maintenance of cells, require
a highly integrated regulation of metabolic processes. However, before examining these regulatory mechanisms, we should define
growth and also differentiation, one of the most fundamental and
fascinating problems of biology.

■ GROWTH AND DIFFERENTIATION

Growth is an increase in mass which can result either from an enlargement of cells or, more often, by an increase through mitotic division
in the number of cells. Growth, then, is essentially a process of replication; the original cell takes from its environment the raw materials it needs and converts them into more substance and more cells
like itself.

Growth, however, is not just the multiplication of cells. In most
organisms it is a complicated pattern of multiplication with different
centers of growth being active both at different times and at different
rates during development. All the parts of an organism increase in a
carefully regulated manner; and when a child grows into an adult,
his organs increase harmoniously. Even at the cellular level, if a cell
doubles its size, the size of the nucleus and cytoplasmic organelles
generally increase in proportion to one another. What are these
regulatory mechanisms? How is growth initiated, and why does it

stop? Biologists have answered some of these questions (see Vol. III), but there are still many problems remaining at the molecular level.

The area of investigation, however, that has aroused perhaps the greatest interest among modern biologists is *differentiation*. We know that during the development of multicellular organisms a single cell gives rise to a variety of different cell types, and it is this phenomenon of differential specialization that gives these cells their uniqueness of structure and function.

In some organisms specialization begins with the first few cell divisions, while in others a large number of divisions occur before any progeny cell is fixed in its fate. However, irrespective of the exact time that differentiation occurs, it always results in the transformation of the parental cell into a large number of morphologically different progeny cell types. In addition, this process is usually irreversible, and differentiation and growth tend to be mutually exclusive. The more specialized a cell becomes, the less likely it is to divide. The problems and implications of differentiation are illustrated well by T. M. Sonneborn who writes:

We are all aware that a human being starts life as a single cell, a fertilized egg. The egg divides into two cells, then each of these into two more, and so on through many successive cell divisions until the more than 10^{15} cellular building blocks of the human body have been formed. Even this is not the end, for cell divisions continue in certain organs and tissues throughout life. During development, the first cells to arise seem to be identical but soon diversities appear. At first they are relatively slight, and generalized, but later the cellular differences become greater and greater, yielding more and more specialized cell types. For example, nerve cells are specialized for transmission of signals and muscle cells for contraction. Finally, about 100 different kinds of normal cells can be distinguished by their structure and function. Unfortunately, sometimes abnormal cells such as tumor cells, also arise sooner or later. By differentiation of cells is meant in part this appearance of diversity, both normal and abnormal, among the cell progeny of the egg cell during the whole of the life of the individual. How this increase of heterogeneity occurs and how its marvelously precise and regular ordering in space and time are governed so as to yield at every stage an integrated functioning multicellular individual are among the deepest and most challenging problems of biology.

In this most familiar example, cellular differentiation is associated with cell division and so might be imagined to depend ultimately upon the parceling out of diverse parts of one cell into different daughter cells. But it is important to recognize that cellular differentiation can also occur in the absence of cell division. This happens, for example, as cells grow older. Cellular changes also develop in response to changes in the milieu, including contact with another kind of cell or with its diffusing or circulating products such as hormones. . . .

Formerly, it was assumed that the whole set of genes was active in every cell. Hence, cells that have the same set of genes cannot become diverse by reason of direct genic action. There was indeed every reason to believe and none to disbelieve, that (with minor and negligible exceptions) cells arising by ordinary division from a common ancestral cell had exactly the same set of genes. In the process of cell division, each chromosome replicates exactly, and one of the two identical daughter chromosomes passes to each daughter cell. Thus all the cells of the body, descended from the egg cell, would have the same set of chromosomes and genes. The cell differentiations arising during development therefore appear not to be due to the possession of different genes. Nor, on the assumption that the genes were all performing the same primary actions in all these diverse cells, could the differentiations be due to direct genic action. This view seemed to be reinforced by the occurrence of differentiation within single cells in the absence of cell division, allowing no possibility of change in the set of genes. Hence it seemed useless to consider direct genic action as relevant to the problem of cell differentiation. So, attention was directed away from the genes to the cytoplasm and the cellular milieu. The milieu was often clearly changing and the cytoplasm obviously divided unequally in some cell divisions. These then became the focus of attention.

Yet there was a justifiable feeling of uneasiness. For the whole of development, including its many progressive steps of cell differentiation, was surely hereditary. And, in well studied organisms like the fruit fly or corn, virtually every step in development was shown to be blockable or modified by genic mutations.[1]

This paradox finally was resolved when it became apparent that not all genes in the chromosomes function at the same time, and that each gene is responsive to signals that regulate its degree of activity. Thus cellular differences even among cells with identical sets of genes are due to the activity of different genes in their chromosomes, and differentiation is due ultimately to variable gene activity. By "activity" we mean, of course, the transcription of the part of the DNA molecule corresponding to a particular gene into complementary messenger RNA which, in turn, directs the synthesis of enzymes and other specific polypeptides.

From studies with giant chromosomes from the salivary glands of certain flies (*Drosophila* and *Chironomus*), there is now excellent evidence for differential rates of RNA synthesis by a single chromosome. These giant chromosomes consist of some 1000–4000 chromatids, or single chromosomal fibers, which lie side by side in huge bundles. It has been established that each band (*Fig. 4–7*) is a gene or small group of genes, and, therefore, it is possible in this case actually to see the linear array of genetic units.

During the course of larval development, certain characteristic chromosomal bands become swollen, while others remain unchanged. It has been shown that such swellings, also known as puffs, are associated with RNA synthesis (*Fig. 4–7*). This formation of RNA is DNA-dependent, because it is inhibited by actinomycin D (Chap. 4); and it is influenced in these Dipteran larvae by a sterol hormone, *ecdysone*. The RNA products of different puffs have different base compositions, as one would expect of the products of different genes.

There is also evidence for differential rates of functioning of homologous chromosomes in mammalian cells. It is believed that in female mammals only one of the pair of X chromosomes in each cell is active. Also during development in man striking changes have been observed in the synthesis of the different polypeptides of hemoglobin. Thus the α-chains are synthesized during all stages of development, while each stage has its own specific nonα-chain. During embryonic life these are the ϵ chains of the embryonic hemoglobins, during fetal life the γ-chains of fetal hemoglobin, and during extra-uterine life the β- and δ-chains found in adult hemoglobin. Presumably, the special properties which adapt each hemoglobin to its particular environment are present in the nonα-chain.

Obviously it would be of great interest to know more about cellular devices which are able to block specifically the functioning of almost an entire chromosome. Unfortunately, such studies in higher animals and plants are still in their infancy. Much more is known about control mechanisms in bacteria and other microorganisms, and we must examine these next, with the hope that nature may have chosen mechanisms that are of general application in governing the selective formation of specific proteins. As a matter of fact, there are indications that similar factors may be operative in all living systems, and that these act either at the genetic level by influencing the formation of enzymes, or directly on enzymes by modifying their activities. There is also evidence of a powerful influence exerted by the cytoplasm over nuclear function, but we still know very little about the cytoplasmic component which induces DNA synthesis.

■ ENZYME INDUCTION AND REPRESSION

It has long been known that yeast cells grown on glucose do not ferment galactose, but, that if galactose is added to the medium, such cells after a brief lag period will be able to utilize this sugar. Similarly, it has been shown that *E. coli* cells grown in a medium containing a β-galactoside, such as lactose, contain more than a thousand times more of the enzyme β-galactosidase than cells grown upon other carbon sources. This adaptive phenomenon is known as *enzyme in-*

duction, and enzymes which can be increased in amount by their corresponding substrates (inducers) are known as *inducible enzymes.*

Many examples are known now for microorganisms, and even in mammals certain enzymes (e.g., tryptophan pyrrolase) have been shown to increase in activity in response to administration of their substrates. In addition, substances other than the substrate sometimes can induce enzyme formation. In the case of β-galactosidase, methyl β-galactoside proved to be an excellent inducer but a very poor substrate.

It is recognized also that the induced enzyme is identical with the enzyme protein normally present, and that it can be induced only if the cell already possesses the requisite genetic information. Even though induction is very rapid, the induced enzyme is newly synthesized from amino acids and is not derived from preexisting, high molecular weight precursors. The inducer, therefore, must somehow directly stimulate protein synthesis. Some enzymes, however, cannot be induced. Such *constitutive enzymes* are produced in fixed amounts independent of need.

An entirely different form of response known as *repression* is shown by many enzymes involved in cellular biosynthesis. Thus *E. coli* cells grown in the absence of amino acids contain all the enzymes necessary for their biosynthesis, but these enzymes soon disappear when the corresponding amino acids are added to the growth medium. These *repressible enzymes* are reduced in amount by the presence of their end products. For example, excess of the amino acid, arginine, shuts off the entire pathway leading to its synthesis. This *feedback control* is of special value in organisms which can accommodate only a limited number of enzyme molecules and exist in a rapidly changing environment.

A general mechanism for induction and repression has been proposed by J. Monod of the Pasteur Institute in Paris and his colleagues, F. Jacob and P. Gros. Based in part on experimental evidence and in part on brilliant speculation, it provides a working hypothesis for control mechanisms at the genetic level. It is assumed that there are, in general, two types of genes, *structural genes* and *regulator genes.*

The DNA sequence of the structural gene is transcribed into specific mRNA, and its expression is governed by a specialized genetic segment, *the operator,* which is immediately next to it. Frequently, several adjacent structural genes may be simultaneously controlled by a single operator segment. Thus in *E. coli* the same operator controls the production of β-galactosidase and also β-galactoside permease, an enzyme which catalyzes the entry of β-galactosides into the cell.

Coordinated synthesis is brought about by having the two enzymes coded by adjacent genes, thereby allowing a single mRNA molecule to carry both genetic messages. Such a unit of genetic expression is known as an *operon,* but the several proteins coded by a single mRNA molecule need not be produced in similar numbers. Many more copies of β-galactosidase than of the permease are synthesized, and during virus reproduction far more copies are made of the coat protein than of the viral specific enzymes.

The operon, in turn, is controlled by a macromolecular compound, the *repressor,* whose structure is determined by the regulator gene, a distinct genetic region which is not part of the operon. Each repressor blocks the synthesis of only certain protein molecules and is able to recognize the operator and bind it specifically. It, therefore, inhibits the expression of all genes belonging to the corresponding operon. There are known examples, however, where the products of a single regulator gene can combine with several operons; and also it is conceivable that a repressor may act by combining with mRNA, thus preventing its attachment to the ribosomes.

Repressors can exist in both an active and inactive form, depending on whether they are combined with certain small molecules, the *inducers* and *corepressors.* Thus repressors do not always inhibit the synthesis of their specific protein. The repressor for β-galactosidase, for example, becomes inactive when combined with a β-galactoside (inducer). In contrast, a corepressor changes an inactive repressor into an active form. This can be shown by the addition of amino acids to cells which are adapted to grow in their absence; the synthesis of the enzymes involved in amino acid biosynthesis is rapidly decreased.

Repressors and their specific inducers or corepressors are held together only by relatively weak bonds such as hydrogen bonds, salt linkages, or van der Waals forces (see Vol. I) which can be made rapidly and broken. This is essential for the swift adjustment of the repressor to the physiological needs. Rapid adaptation to a changing environment also is made possible by the metabolic instability of bacterial mRNA. The average lifetime of most *E. coli* mRNA molecules at 37°C is about two minutes after which they are enzymatically broken down. Thus every few minutes there is virtually complete replacement of the templates for many proteins. However, it seems that much of the mRNA of the highly differentiated cells of higher organisms is metabolically stable. Reticulocytes, for example, produce virtually no RNA while they are synthesizing their principal protein, hemoglobin.

Inactivation of a regulator gene or its repressor by mutation results in uncontrolled or "constitutive" enzyme synthesis. The control of protein (enzyme) synthesis is illustrated schematically in *Fig. 5–1.*

Concerning the nature of the repressor, some are thought to be proteins; and histones, in particular, are believed to play such a role.

Thus these basic proteins, which are rich in the amino acids, lysine or arginine, have been shown to diminish nuclear RNA synthesis. In addition, R. C. Huang and J. Bonner, while testing the RNA-polymerase activity of pea-seedling chromatin, observed that DNA-histone complexes were not effective as "primers" of RNA synthesis, and that the rate of RNA production could be increased fivefold by removing the histone. Similarly, V. Allfrey has shown that RNA synthesis in trypsin-treated calf thymus nuclei, in which the histones were degraded, was 300–400 per cent higher than that observed in untreated controls.

Histones occur only in chromatin and thus far have been demonstrated only in those organisms which contain proper chromosomes and which generally differentiate into different types of specialized cells. It is of interest that the activity of the histones themselves in the nucleus may be modified by acetylation or methylation in a way which permits reactivation of previously repressed gene loci.

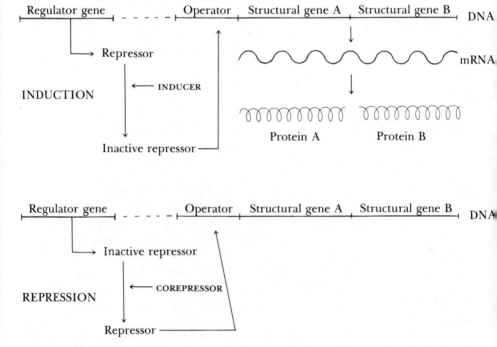

Fig. 5–1. Postulated mechanism for the control of protein (enzyme) synthesis. Protein formation is inhibited until the inducer combines with the repressor and converts it into an inactive form (induction). In contrast, a corepressor converts an inactive repressor into an active molecule (repression). No repressor is present to control constitutive protein synthesis.

Jacob and Monod summarize their proposed mechanism for the genetic regulation of protein synthesis in the following manner:

> The synthesis of enzymes in bacteria follows a double genetic control. The so-called structural genes determine the molecular organization of the proteins. Other, functionally specialized, genetic determinants, called regulator and operator genes, control the rate of protein synthesis through the intermediacy of cytoplasmic components or repressors. The repressors can be either inactivated (induction) or activated (repression) by certain specific metabolites. This system of regulation appears to operate directly at the level of the synthesis by the gene of a short-lived intermediate, or messenger, which becomes associated with the ribosomes where protein synthesis takes place.

They add:

> These conclusions apply strictly to the bacterial systems from which they were derived; but the fact that adaptive enzyme systems of both types (inducible and repressible) and phage systems appear to obey the same fundamental mechanism of control, involving the same essential elements, argues strongly for the generality of what may be called "repressive genetic regulation" of protein synthesis.
>
> One is led to wonder whether all or most structural genes (i.e. the synthesis of most proteins) are submitted to repressive regulation. In bacteria, virtually all the enzyme systems which have been adequately studied have proved sensitive to inductive or repressive effects. The old idea that such effects are characteristic only of "non-essential" enzymes is certainly incorrect although, of course, these effects can be detected only under conditions, natural or artificial, such that the system under study is at least partially non-essential. The results of mutations which abolish the control (such as constitutive mutations) illustrate its physiological importance. Constitutive mutants of the lactose system synthesize 6 to 7% of all their proteins as β-galactosidase. In constitutive mutants of the phosphatase system, 5 to 6% of the total protein is phosphatase. Similar figures have been obtained with other constitutive mutants. It is clear that the cells could not survive the breakdown of more than two or three of the control systems which keep in pace the synthesis of enzyme proteins.
>
> The occurrence of inductive and repressive effects in tissues of higher organisms has been observed in many instances although it has not proved possible so far to analyze any of these systems in detail. It has repeatedly been pointed out that enzymatic adaptation, as studied in micro-organisms, offers a valuable model for the interpretation of biochemical coordination within tissues and between organs in higher organisms. The demonstration that adaptive effects in micro-organisms are primarily negative (repressive), that they are controlled by functionally specialized genes and operate at the genetic level, would seem greatly to widen the possibilities of inter-

pretation. The fundamental problem of chemical physiology and of embryology is to understand why tissue cells do not express, all the time, all the potentialities inherent in their genome. The survival of the organism requires that many, and, in some tissues most, of these potentialities be unexpressed, that is to say *repressed.* Malignancy is adequately described as a breakdown of one or several growth controlling systems, and the genetic origin of this breakdown can hardly be doubted.

According to the strictly structural concept, the genome is considered as a mosaic of independent molecular blue-prints for the building of the individual cellular constituents. In the execution of these plans, however, coordination is evidently of absolute survival value. The discovery of regulator and operator genes, and of repressive regulation of the activity of structural genes, reveals that the genome contains not only a series of blue-prints but a co-ordinated program of protein synthesis and the means of controlling its execution.[2]

■ FEEDBACK CONTROL OF ENZYME ACTIVITY

In previous chapters we have seen how the synthesis of most biological products requires a series of steps, each of which is catalyzed by a specific enzyme. The output of a given substance, therefore, can be controlled either by changing the number of enzyme molecules available for some step in the chain (induction or repression) or by altering their catalytic properties (activation or inhibition). As we have considered already the mechanisms that control the manufacture of enzymes, let us turn now to the regulation of their activity.

A good demonstration of such control has been obtained in experiments with bacteria. It has been shown that overproduction of isoleucine in *E. coli* is prevented not only by a decrease in the formation of all the enzymes needed for its synthesis but also by the inhibition by isoleucine of threonine deaminase, an enzyme which catalyzes the first step in the chain of reactions leading to the formation of isoleucine. Such a control mechanism, in which the final product inhibits an enzyme concerned in an early step of its own biosynthesis, is known as *feedback inhibition.* Like the temperature level in a house with a thermostatically regulated heating system, the level of isoleucine in the cell exerts a negative feedback control on its own production (*Fig. 5–2*).

The isoleucine control system in *E. coli* is only one example of this type of regulation in the living cell. It has been shown now that similar circuits control not only the cell's production of other amino acids but also the purine and pyrimidine precursors of DNA and RNA. Although the control of isoleucine synthesis is negative, involving the inhibition of an enzyme, the opposite situation is also known in which the control system activates an enzyme. Thus in the synthesis of

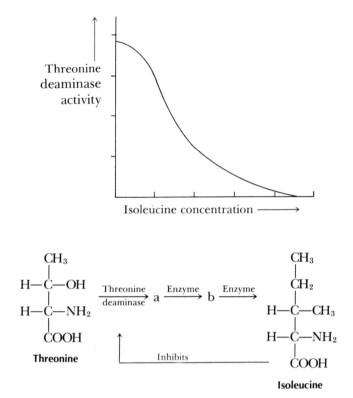

Fig. 5–2. End-product inhibition of isoleucine synthesis from threonine.

glycogen, glucose-6-phosphate, a precursor of this storage polysaccharide, activates the enzyme that converts uridine diphosphate glucose into glycogen (*Fig. 4–1*).

Another example showing that certain enzymes, in addition to their purely catalytic function, may act as regulators of metabolic pathways, is illustrated by the classical studies of Cori and his group on muscle phosphorylase (Chap. 4). This enzyme can exist in two states one of which (phosphorylase a) is fully active, while the other (phosphorylase b) is active only in the presence of cyclic adenylic acid. The two states are interconvertible through phosphorylation, which converts phosphorylase b into phosphorylase a, and dephosphorylation, which reverses this process. This system, which is of primary importance for regulating the release of energy during muscular contraction, is controlled by the cellular level of cyclic AMP which, in turn, is under hormonal control (discussed later).

The role of adenylates (ATP, ADP, and AMP) in the regulation of energy metabolism has been discussed fully by D. E. Atkinson who writes:

> Most metabolic energy-converting or energy-coupling processes occur at the expense of adenosine triphosphate (ATP) which is converted to adenosine-5'-monophosphate (AMP) or adenosine diphosphate (ADP). Regeneration of ATP is one of the major functions of both

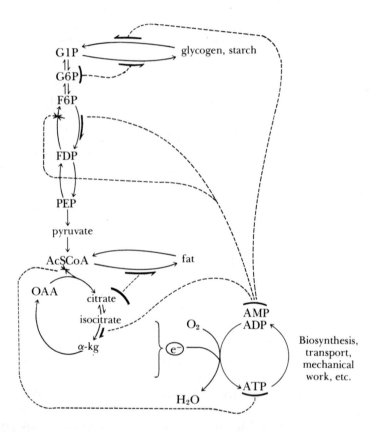

Fig. 5-3. Schematic illustration of the role proposed for AMP, ADP, and ATP in regulation of energy metabolism. Broken lines connect effector compounds (indicated by heavy arcs) to the enzymes which they modulate. Positive effector action is denoted by a heavy arrow, and negative effector action by a heavy cross. Abbreviations in addition to those defined in the text are: G1P, glucose-1-phosphate; G6P, glucose-6-phosphate; F6P, fructose-6-phosphate; FDP, fructose-1,6-diphosphate; PEP, phosphoenolpyruvate; AcSCoA, acetyl coenzyme A; α-kg, α-ketoglutarate; OAA, oxaloacetate. Supply of electrons (from oxidative reactions in the glycolytic and Krebs cycle pathways) to the electron transport phosphorylation system is indicated by the symbol e^-. ("Biological Feedback Control at the Molecular Level," D. E. Atkinson, *Science,* Vol. 150, pp. 851–857, Fig. 2, 12 November 1965. Copyright 1965 by the American Association for the Advancement of Science.)

oxidative and fermentative metabolism. Since the concentrations of AMP and ATP will be inversely related in the intact cell, stimulation by AMP corresponds in metabolic terms to negative feedback by ATP. A number of recent observations suggest that both inhibition by ATP and stimulation by AMP play important roles in the regulation of energy metabolism. . . . This schematic illustration (*Fig. 5–3*) may be considered as a first step towards the production of a regulatory metabolic map corresponding to the maps that have been prepared to show metabolic sequences.

Like them, it is summary and superficial rather than specific and detailed. It does not take intracellular compartmentation into account, and the effects shown have not all been demonstrated in a single type of cell. It shows how several enzyme modulations may function in determining the momentary balance between oxidative metabolism and energy storage, and illustrates the hypothesis that the concentration of AMP is a major metabolic control variable. If the interrelationships suggested in this figure remain tenable, it is reasonable to expect that AMP will be found to modulate the action of other enzymes such as those that catalyze first steps in the degradation of optional energy sources. A high concentration of AMP might thus serve as an emergency signal causing amino acids, for example, to be diverted from their normal role in protein synthesis when the energy needs of the cell are extreme. The positive effector action of AMP and ADP on threonine and serine dehydrase (deaminase) may be an example of this type of regulation.

A much more inclusive map could already be drawn on the basis of present knowledge. Many cell constituents, including purines, pyrimidines, and most amino acids, are biosynthesized from intermediates of this pathway, and in nearly all cases an early step in the synthesis has been shown to be governed by feedback control, usually with the end product serving as the negative effector. At least suggestive evidence is also available regarding the regulation of other metabolic processes by similar mechanisms.[3]

■ ALLOSTERIC INTERACTIONS

The final product in a biosynthetic sequence is separated generally from its initial precursor by several intermediate metabolic steps, and an end product inhibitor is, therefore, unlikely to resemble structurally the substrate of the enzyme which it inhibits. This means that one would not expect feedback inhibition to occur by a reaction involving the active site (see Vol. I) of the inhibited enzyme. Instead, it is believed that the inhibitor combines with some other site on the enzyme and acts by causing a change in the precise shape of the enzyme, thereby preventing it from combining with its substrate. Proteins which are capable of changing shape as a result of binding specific small molecules at sites other than the active site are known as *allosteric proteins*, and those small molecules that bring about allosteric transformations are called *allosteric effectors* (*Fig. 5–4*). Monod has suggested that the enzyme molecule consists of a set of identical subunits, and that it can switch back and forth between two states which differ in the energy of binding between the subunits. In the more relaxed state the enzyme molecule preferentially binds substrate, while in the more constrained state it binds inhibitor. Whichever compound it binds will tip the balance to favor the binding of that category of small molecule, so that a change in the relative concentrations of substrate and inhibitor may tip the balance one way or the other.

In order to exert feedback control, the reactions must be freely reversible and, as in the postulated repressor-corepressor union (p. 95), the binding is believed to involve weak secondary forces such as hydrogen bonds, salt linkage, and van der Waals forces, rather than covalent bonds. Allosteric effectors may function as activators as well as inhibitors.

Thus it appears that control and regulation by regulatory enzymes depends on the form of their molecular structure into which is built, as into a computer, the capacity to recognize and integrate various signals. In the words of Monod:

> An allosteric protein is in fact to be considered as a specialized product of selective engineering, allowing an indirect interaction, positive or negative, to take place between metabolites which otherwise would not or even could not interact in any way, thus eventually bringing a particular reaction under the control of a chemically foreign or indifferent compound. In this way it is possible to understand how, by selection of adequate allosteric protein structures, any physiologically useful controlling connection between any pathways in a cell may have become established. It is hardly necessary to point out that the integrated chemical functioning of a cell requires that such controlling systems should exist. The important point for our present discussion is that these circuits of control could not have evolved if their elementary mechanisms had been restricted to *direct* chemical interaction (including direct interactions on an enzyme site) between different pathways. By using certain proteins not only as catalysts or transporters but as molecular receivers and transducers of chemical signals, freedom is gained from otherwise insuperable chemical constraints, allowing selection to develop and interconnect the immensely complex circuitry of living organisms.[4]

■ OTHER CONTROLLING FACTORS

So far, we have considered only some of the factors which control the highly integrated metabolic reactions of living cells. We must remember also that many enzymes are for the most part firmly asso-

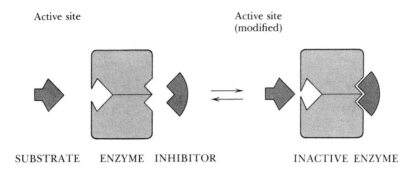

Active site   Active site
                                      (modified)

SUBSTRATE   ENZYME INHIBITOR   INACTIVE ENZYME

Fig. 5–4. Schematic representation of an allosteric transformation. The inhibitor causes a change in the shape of the enzyme and thereby modifies the active site.

ciated with cytoplasmic structures. Thus the electron transport system of the cell is interlocked with the enzymes of oxidative phosphorylation in a highly organized manner on the mitochondrial membranes or cristae. Physical factors, such as changes in the osmotic conditions of the surrounding medium or in the permeability of the mitochondrial membrane, may affect the structural organization of the enzymes within these organelles and produce marked changes in the normal sequence of metabolic events.

Another consideration is the special separation of multienzyme systems from each other. In the degradation of glucose to carbon dioxide and water, the glycolytic enzymes are found outside the mitochondria; however, a close partnership must be maintained between this metabolic sequence and the reactions of the tricarboxylic acid cycle which occur within them. Any interference in this partnership, or any change in the concentration of phosphate and magnesium ions, or the ratio of ADP to ATP, or NAD to $NADH_2$, will result in a modification of glucose metabolism.

Another factor in metabolic control and regulation is the ability of subcellular organelles to concentrate coenzymes and substrates far above the concentration found outside these particles. This is well illustrated by mitochondria which can be made to swell and contract by a variety of agents including hormones (see below). This pulsating phenomenon, which occurs in mitochondria even in the intact cell, brings about changes in permeability to extramitochondrial metabolites and intramitochondrial ATP. When the external ATP/ADP ratio is high, mitochondria remain in a contracted, less permeable state; access to oxidizable substrates and leakage of intramitochondrial ATP is diminished. When the external ATP concentration declines, ATP is lost from mitochondria; and the permeability to substrate increases, leading to oxidation and formation of ATP. This swelling-contraction is, therefore, another example of the many cybernetic mechanisms permitting self-adjustment of energy production in the living cell.

Integration and order in metabolism is also accomplished by a functional division between synthetic and degradative pathways which are now recognized to be catalyzed generally by different multienzyme systems. Even when some of the individual enzymes are used in common for both processes, the two systems are differentiated by at least one reaction which is irreversible and, therefore, functions as a one-way gate. This separation of anabolic and catabolic reactions, with the inclusion in each of at least one irreversible step, provides regulatory mechanisms which could not exist in freely reversible systems.

Yet another parameter of control is exerted through supply and demand. Thus certain products of carbohydrate metabolism aid in the combustion of fats. Intermediates of nucleic acid metabolism are cofactors required for carbohydrate degradation, and these, in turn, provide the sugar component of the nucleic acids. These complex interactions are controlled by the amount of the individual enzymes present, their ability to compete for shared cofactors, and the supply of energy. The recent findings, that chain initiation in protein synthesis is dependent on a formylation reaction in which formylmethionine is produced, places nucleic acid and protein synthesis under the common control of the supply of one-carbon compounds (see Vol. I). In addition, the synthesis of protein becomes critically dependent upon cofactors involved in formyl transfer, such as pyridoxal phosphate and tetrahydrofolic acid.

Finally, at the tissue level, growth is controlled also by *contact inhibition* between cells. Abercrombie and others have shown that when cells are grown on a glass surface, their normal movements are inhibited at the point of contact with each other, leading eventually to the formation of a monolayer of cells. As the cells multiply and as the proportion of the cell surface in contact with other cells increases, there is a pronounced decrease in RNA, DNA and protein synthesis, and in the rate of cellular growth. Simultaneously, the free cytoplasmic polysomes present in growing cells are no longer demonstrable. All these effects can be reversed within 24 hours by subdividing the cultures, and it appears that the cellular contact itself sets off a series of reactions, beginning in the surface membrane and ending with a decreased rate of macromolecular synthesis.

■ HORMONAL CONTROL

The role of hormones in differentiation and metabolic regulation now is well established but very little is known about the manner in which these substances exert their varied effects. For a while it was believed that some of the steroid hormones and, in particular, the estrogens (female sex hormones) acted as coenzymes by shuttling hydrogen between NAD and NADP; but although this effect on "transhydrogenation" is demonstrable *in vitro,* evidence that it is an important physiological mechanism has not been forthcoming.

Nevertheless, because of the latent period of hormone action, the extremely low concentrations required to produce physiological effects and their high degree of specificity in action *in vivo,* hormones are believed to function by controlling either the synthesis or activation of enzymes. G. M. Tomkins has made the interesting observation that estrogens can cause a reversible disaggregation of enzymes such as glutamic dehydrogenase into inactive subunits, and E. W. Sutherland has shown that the hormones *adrenaline* (from the adrenal medulla) and *glucagon* (from the α-islet cells of the pancreas) exert their glycogenolytic effect by increasing the concentration of the active form of phosphorylase (Chap. 3). This reaction, which produces a rapid increase in blood glucose concentration, is indirect and involves cyclic adenylic acid as shown below (*Fig. 5–5*).

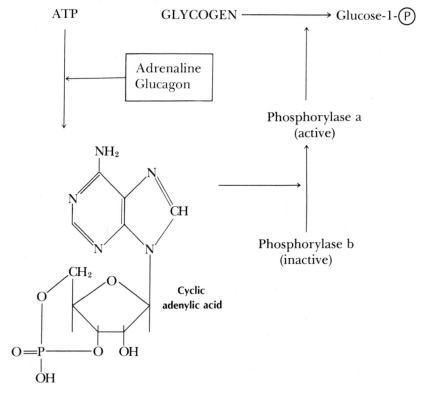

Fig. 5–5. The action of adrenaline and glucagon in the breakdown of glycogen.

It has been suggested also that hormones modify the outer membrane of cells and directly affect the physical state of structures within the cell. Experiments with the pituitary hormone *vasopressin,* which causes blood vessels to constrict and increases water reabsorption by the kidneys, strongly support the conclusion that this hormone attaches itself to the outer membrane of the cell on which it acts. There is now general agreement that insulin exerts some of its effects by increasing the penetration of cell membranes by glucose as well as by activating the enzymes which catalyze the metabolism of this sugar.

However, more recently a growing body of evidence is accumulating which suggests that many hormones act by altering the pattern of genetic activity (expression) in the cells responsive to them. Thus injection of the insect moulting hormone *ecdysone* into young Chironomus larvae will produce within 15 minutes a succession of "puffs" in certain chromosomal areas. These "puffs" have been shown to be associated with DNA-dependent RNA synthesis and are believed to be derepressed genes. The RNA produced in different puffs have different base composition, as one would expect of the products of different genes. In addition, messenger RNA from ecdysone-treated larvae causes the production of an enzyme, dihydroxyphenylalanine (DOPA) decarboxylase, while messenger RNA from control larvae not treated with the hormone does not elicit the synthesis of this enzyme.

These findings demonstrate that the action of the hormone is to cause production of a new species of messenger RNA (see also Vol. IV). Similarly, during germination the plant hormone *gibberellic acid* derepresses the gene for making α-amylase in the endosperm of barley seed. It causes the target organ to produce a specific enzyme in greatly increased amount; and this process, which is preceded by an increase in RNA synthesis, is inhibited by actinomycin D and is, therefore, DNA-dependent.

In mammals, too, hormones have been shown to have similar effects on the "target" tissues. The injection of estrogen, for example, into an immature or ovariectomized rat results in a tenfold increase in the rate of RNA production in the cells of the uterus within 30 minutes of treatment, followed by a considerable rise in protein synthesis. However, these and other metabolic changes do not occur in the presence of actinomycin D, showing that estrogen is acting at the DNA (gene) level.

In order to account for the many different responses of the cells to estrogen, a considerable number of genes must be activated. This, however, raises a problem of gene regulation: how can a single hormone activate an entire set of functionally related but otherwise quite separate genes and activate them in a specific sequence? Similar questions arise in considering one of the effects of estrogens in birds.

When an egg is formed in a hen, the estrogens of its ovaries stimulate its liver to produce the yolk proteins lipovitellin and phosvitin. Normally, a rooster does not synthesize these proteins; but it will produce them in large amounts if treated with this female sex hormone, and the effect is remarkably specific.

E. N. Carlsen and his group in Los Angeles have shown that estrogen most strongly stimulates liver cells to produce the particular transfer RNA which is associated with the incorporation of serine into protein. This amino acid accounts for almost half the amino acid subunits in phosvitin. Thus the effect of estrogen on liver cells (in birds) is quite different from its effect on uterine cells, and it is now well established that hormonal specificity resides less in the hormone than in the "target cell."

How is the set of genes selected that is activated by a given hormone? Are these genes somehow preset for hormonal activation? Many more questions could be asked and many more examples could be given showing the action of hormones of different types at the gene level, but space does not allow this intriguing topic to be pursued further. It does seem, however, that hormones act in many cases, perhaps in all, as agents which control genetic activity. Through the study of hormone-gene interaction, we may hope to gain understanding of the nature of genetic switching devices and, indirectly, of metabolic control.

■ CONTROL MECHANISMS: EPILOGUE

The present status of our knowledge of control processes is summarized by Atkinson:

> Our present situation with regard to understanding metabolic control might be compared to that of a visitor from a different culture who, though not quite able to comprehend the regulation of a thermostatic water bath, tries without guide or guidebook to understand the control system of a modern satellite. We can rationalize in terms of apparent regulatory function the observation that the catalytic activities of several enzymes are modulated by metabolites. The metabolic relationships between the regulatory metabolites and the enzymes, and the interrelations between the enzymes that are so modulated, are such as to give us a high degree of confidence that our rationalizations are at least partially correct. But most of the apparently regulatory enzymes, as studied *in vitro*, are strongly influenced also by changes in pH, and many of them by the concentration of various cations. Since we have no way of estimating the extent to which the local pH or activities of cations may vary in the cell, we cannot even guess to what extent these parameters participate in metabolic regulation. It seems likely that in the intact cell most en-

zymes are attached to structural elements and so have a more or less definite spatial relationship to other enzymes. The observed kinetic modulations of regulatory enzymes are generally assumed to be accompanied by changes in the conformations of the enzyme molecules. Such changes must alter the relation of an enzyme to other enzymes as well as to other functional elements in the cell, and alterations within a living cell are not likely to occur randomly. It would be surprising if regulatory enzymes had not evolved in such a way that the physical consequences of effector modulation would reinforce the chemical aspects of regulation. Life is notable for the intensity and complexity of its component chemical reactions, but a more specific characteristic is a harmonious self-regulation in the face of drastic changes in external conditions and of the still more drastic threat of internal chaos. This regulation must require far more in the way of molecular and supramolecular specificity than does the simple catalysis of the reactions themselves, and it is likely that most of the genetic information transmitted to daughter cells relates to this area of which we as yet understand almost nothing. Metabolic chemistry is in its infancy. To paraphrase Newton's famous metaphor, we have amused ourselves with the shiny pebbles of metabolic sequences (and the smaller pebbles of individual enzymic reactions) while before us lay largely unperceived the ocean of interrelation and regulation. We do not yet really understand any of our pebbles, and we have only begun to notice a bit of salt spray in the air.[5]

1. T. M. Sonneborn, "The Differentiation of Cells," *Proceedings of the National Academy of Sciences*, 51 (1964), 915–925.
2. F. Jacob and J. Monod, "Genetic Regulatory Mechanisms in the Synthesis of Protein," *Journal of Molecular Biology*, 3 (1961), 318–356.
3. "Biological Feedback Control at the Molecular Level," D. E. Atkinson, *Science*, Vol. 150 (pp. 851–857 inclusive), p. 851, 12 November 1965. Copyright 1965 by the American Association for the Advancement of Science.
4. Jacques Monod, "On the Mechanism and Molecular Interactions in the Control of Cellular Metabolism," *Endocrinology*, 78 (1966), 412.
5. Atkinson, *op. cit.*, p. 851.

SELECTED READINGS

CHAPTER 1

Beck, W. S. *Modern Science and the Nature of Life.* New York: Harcourt, Brace, and World, Inc., 1957.

Brachet, J. "The Living Cell," *Scientific American*, 205 (September 1961), 50–61.

De Duve, Christian. "The Lysosome," *Scientific American*, 208 (May 1963), 64–83.

———. "Lysosomes, A New Group of Cytoplasmic Particles," in *Subcellular Particles*, ed. T. Hayashi. New York: Ronald Press Company, 1959.

Dippell, R. V. "Ultrastructure and Function," in *This is Life*, ed. W. H. Johnson and W. C. Steere. New York: Holt, Rinehart and Winston, Inc., 1962.

Fawcett, D. W. *An Atlas of Fine Structure: The Cell, Its Organelles and Inclusions.* Philadelphia: W. B. Saunders Co., 1966.

Green, D. E. "Mitochondrial Structure and Function," in *Subcellular Particles*, ed. T. Hayashi. New York: Ronald Press Company, 1959.

———. "The Mitochondrion," *Scientific American*, 210 (January 1964), 63–78.

Green, D. E. and O. Hechter. "Assembly of Membrane Subunits," *Proceedings of the National Academy of Sciences*, 53 (1965), 318–325.

Hokin, L. E. and M. R. Hokin. "The Chemistry of Cell Membranes," *Scientific American*, 213 (October 1965), 78–87.

Holter, H. "How Things Get into Cells," *Scientific American*, 205 (September 1961), 167–183.

Korn, E. A. "Structure of Biological Membranes," *Science*, 153 (1966), 1491–1498.

Lehninger, A. L. *The Mitochondrion: Molecular Basis of Structure and Function.* New York: W. A. Benjamin, Inc., 1964.

Loewy, A. G. and P. Siekevitz. *Cell Structure and Function.* New York: Holt, Rinehart and Winston, Inc., 1963.

McLaren, A. D. and K. L. Babcock. "Some Characteristics of Enzyme Reactions at Surfaces," in *Subcellular Particles*, ed. T. Hayashi. New York: Ronald Press Company, 1959.

Ritchie and Hazeltine, in D. Haldar, K. Freeman, and T. S. Work. "Biogenesis of Mitochondria," *Nature*, 211 (1966), 9–12.

Robertson, J. D. "The Membrane of the Living Cell," *Scientific American*, 206 (April 1962), 64–83.

Siegel, A. "Reproduction and Heredity," in *This is Life*, ed. W. H. Johnson and W. C. Steere. New York: Holt, Rinehart and Winston, Inc., 1962.

Stent, G. S. *Molecular Biology of Bacterial Viruses*. San Francisco: W. H. Freeman and Co., 1963.

Swanson, C. P. *The Cell*. Englewood Cliffs, New Jersey: Prentice-Hall, Inc., 1960.

CHAPTER 2

Baldwin, E. *An Introduction to Comparative Biochemistry*. 4th ed. Cambridge: Cambridge University Press, 1964.

————. *Dynamic Aspects of Biochemistry*. 4th ed. Cambridge: Cambridge University Press, 1963.

Francis, G. E., W. Mulligan, and A. Wormall. *Isotopic Tracers*. 2nd ed. London: Athlone Press, 1959.

Green, D. E. and S. Fleisher. "On the Molecular Organization of Biological Transducing Systems," in *Horizons in Biochemistry*, ed. M. Kasha and B. Pullman. New York: Academic Press, Inc., 1962.

Kamen, Martin D. "Tracers," *Scientific American*, 180 (February 1949), 30–41.

Krebs, H. A. "Cyclic Processes in Living Matter," *Enzymologia*, 12 (1946), 97–100.

Lehninger, A. L. *Bioenergetics: The Molecular Basis of Biological Energy Transformations*. New York: W. A. Benjamin, Inc., 1965.

Schoenheimer, R. *The Dynamic State of Body Constituents*, rev. Hans T. Clarke, David Rittenberg, and Sarah Ratner. Cambridge, Massachusetts: Harvard University Press, 1942.

White, A., P. Handler, and E. L. Smith. *Principles of Biochemistry*. 3rd ed. New York: McGraw-Hill, Inc., 1964.

CHAPTER 3

Arnon, D. I., H. Y. Tsujimoto, and B. D. McSwain. "Photosynthetic Phosphorylation and Electron Transport," *Nature*, 207 (1965), 1367.

Conn, E. E. and P. K. Stumpf. *Outlines of Biochemistry*. New York: John Wiley & Sons, Inc., 1963.

Griffiths, E. D. "Oxidative Phosphorylation," in *Essays in Biochemistry*, ed. P. N. Campbell and G. D. Greville. Vol. I. New York: Academic Press, Inc., 1965.

Hill, R. "The Biochemists' Green Mansions: The Photosynthetic Electron-Transport Chain in Plants," in *Essays in Biochemistry*, ed. P. N. Campbell and G. D. Greville. Vol. I. New York: Academic Press, Inc., 1965.

Karlson, P. *Introduction to Modern Biochemistry*. 2nd ed. New York: Academic Press, Inc., 1965.

Krebs, H. A. and W. A. Johnson. "The Role of Citric Acid in Intermediary Metabolism," *Enzymologia*, 4 (1937), 151–152.

Racker, E. *Mechanisms in Bioenergetics*. New York: Academic Press, Inc., 1965.

Sistrom, W. R. *Microbal Life*. New York: Holt, Rinehart and Winston, Inc., 1962.

Wood, H. G. and M. F. Utter. "The Role of CO_2 Fixation in Metabolism," in *Essays in Biochemistry*, ed. P. N. Campbell and G. D. Greville. Vol. I. New York: Academic Press, Inc., 1965.

CHAPTER 4

Anfinsen, C. B. *The Molecular Basis of Evolution.* New York: John Wiley & Sons, Inc., 1959.
Arnstein, H. R. V. "Mechanisms of Protein Biosynthesis," *British Medical Bulletin*, 21 (1965), 217–222.
Cain, D. F. and R. E. Davies. "Breakdown of Adenosine Triphosphate During a Single Contraction of Working Muscle," *Biochemical and Biophysical Research Communications*, 8 (1962), 361.
Chapeville, F., F. Lipmann, G. von Ehrenstein, B. Weisblum, W. J. Ray, and S. Benzer. "On the Role of Soluble RNA in Coding for Amino Acids," *Proceedings of the National Academy of Sciences*, 48 (1962), 1086.
Crick, F. H. C. "The Biochemistry of Genetics," *Proceedings of the Plenary Sessions of the 6th International Congress of Biochemistry*, New York (1964), 109.
————. "The Genetic Code," *Scientific American*, 207 (October 1962), 66–77.
Hanson, J. and J. Lowy. "Molecular Basis of Contractility in Muscle," *British Medical Bulletin*, 21 (1965), 264–271.
Hartman, P. E. and S. R. Suskind. *Gene Action.* Englewood Cliffs, New Jersey: Prentice-Hall, Inc., 1965.
Huxley, H. E. "The Mechanism of Muscular Contraction," *Scientific American*, 213 (December 1965), 18–27.
Ingram, V. M. *The Biosynthesis of Macromolecules.* New York: W. A. Benjamin, Inc., 1965.
Leloir, L. F. "The Biosynthesis of Polysaccharides," *Proceedings of the Plenary Sessions of the 6th International Congress of Biochemistry*, New York (1964), 15.
McElroy, W. D. *Cell Physiology and Biochemistry.* 2nd ed. Englewood Cliffs, New Jersey: Prentice-Hall, Inc., 1964.
Nirenberg, Marshall W. "The Genetic Code: II," *Scientific American*, 208 (March 1963), 80–95.
Smellie, R. M. S. "Biochemistry of Deoxyribonucleic Acid and Ribonucleic Acid Replication," *British Medical Bulletin*, 21 (1965), 195–202.
Stretton, A. O. W. "The Genetic Code," *British Medical Bulletin*, 21 (1965), 229–235.
Sutton, H. E. *Genes, Enzymes and Inherited Diseases.* New York: Holt, Rinehart and Winston, Inc., 1961.
Von Ehrenstein, G. and F. Lipmann. "Experiments on Hemoglobin Biosynthesis," *Proceedings of the National Academy of Sciences*, 47 (1961), 941.

CHAPTER 5

Atkinson, D. E. "Biological Feedback Control at the Molecular Level," *Science*, 150 (1965), 851–857.

Beermann, W. and U. Clever. "Chromosomes Puffs," *Scientific American*, 210 (April 1964), 50–65.

Bonner, James. *The Molecular Biology of Development*. New York: Oxford University Press, 1965.

Brenner, S. "Theories of Gene Regulation," *British Medical Bulletin*, 21 (1965), 244–248.

Changeux, J. P. "The Control of Biochemical Reactions," *Scientific American*, 212 (April 1965), 36–45.

Davidson, Eric H. "Hormones and Genes," *Scientific American*, 212 (June 1965), 36–45.

Eagle, H. "Metabolic Controls in Cultured Mammalian Cells," *Science*, 148 (1965), 42–50.

Ebert, J. D. *Interacting Systems in Development*. New York: Holt, Rinehart and Winston, Inc., 1965.

Jacob, F. and J. Monod. "Genetic Regulatory Mechanisms in the Synthesis of Proteins," *Journal of Molecular Biology*, 3 (1961), 318–356.

Monod, J. "On the Mechanism and Molecular Interactions in the Control of Cellular Metabolism," *Endocrinology*, 78 (1966), 412.

Sonneborn, T. M. "The Differentiation of Cells," *Proceedings of the National Academy of Sciences*, 51 (1964), 915–925.

Watson, J. D. *Molecular Biology of the Gene*. New York: W. A. Benjamin, Inc., 1965.

INDEX